T-60

SMALL TANK AND VARIANTS

CONTENTS

Red Machines Vol.1 T-60 Small Tank and Variants

©Canfora Publishing 2017
ISBN 978-91-982325-6-1
Project Manager: James Kinnear
Design: Toni Canfora
Print: Printbest, Tallinn, Estonia

Canfora Publishing/Canfora Grafisk Form
Upplandsgatan 96A
113 44 Stockholm, Sweden
www.canfora.se
info@canfora.se

INTRODUCTION

The T-60 small tank was in terms of production output the third most numerous tank-type built in the Soviet Union during the 1941-45 "Great Patriotic War", behind only the T-34 medium tank and the SU-76 self propelled gun. Though often maligned in later years as being under-armed and under-armoured, the T-60 performed a crucial role during the difficult years of 1941-42 when Soviet manufacturing plants struggled to replace combat losses at the front. The T-60 participated in most theatres of the war on Soviet soil in the years 1941-44, including the Defence of Moscow, the Siege of Leningrad and the Battle of Stalingrad. As such, the T-60 tank, of which nearly 6000 were produced during 1941-42, was far from an obscure small production tank with limited combat service, and yet until recently the T-60 tank was not well researched either at home in the Russian Federation or abroad, being (together with the T-30 and T-40 from which it was derived) the least researched Soviet tanks of the Second World War. This volume for the first time in English redresses the situation with a comprehensive account of the T-60 tank, the plants where it was assembled, combat history and the numerous production and prototype variants built on the T-60 chassis.

This study is the result of several years of archival research in the Russian Federation and is based almost entirely on contemporary Russian primary source material. Over the past decade, much material that was previously stamped "Secret" even though many decades old, was declassified and became available for research purposes. The most valuable recently declassified material is the large volume of material from the archives of the Main Armoured Directorate of the Red Army (GABTU KA) within the Central Archives of the Ministry of Defence of the Russian Federation (TsAMO RF) located in the town of Podolsk in the Moscow suburbs. Material was also made available from the Russian State Archive of Economics (RGAE) and the Russian State Archive of Socio-Political History (RGASPI).

Access to such a wealth of original primary source archive material has allowed the development, production and Red Army service life of the T-60 to be better understood, and also placed more in perspective with its time in service and its role.

The material has also remedied some previous assumptions and in cases outright distortions based on a lack of such source material in the past, albeit the authors accept that some original source material remains conflated and the story will continue to unravel as additional material comes to light.

One indicator of the limited research into the topic of the smaller Soviet tanks of the Second World War period is that the T-60 has always been historically classified as a "light" tank; whereas the tank was classified as "small" by the Red Army. The boundary between Soviet small and light tanks was during the 1930s in the region of 3-3.5 metric tonnes. Further, in the majority of contemporary Soviet official correspondence, the T-60 is defined simply as the "T-60" without further type classification. In the structure of tank brigades and tank corps in 1941-42, the T-60 is referred to specifically as a small tank, as is the T-70 that ultimately replaced it. An indication of the reasoning behind this nuance is described in a Soviet training manual dated 1940, which states:

"Small tanks (which can be amphibious) are for the most part intended for combined arms reconnaissance and for strengthening combined arms reconnaissance units. Small tanks are also used for communication and for the transport of anti-tank guns. In mechanized combat small tanks can be used to support infantry and cavalry. The possibility of using them in the attack is not excluded (except against strengthened positions) but only after breakthrough by gun armed light tanks. Small tanks can be used in various defensive roles and in forced river crossings*.

The T-60 was a "small" tank, but in the dark years of 1941-42 it performed a vital infantry support role, at a time when tank losses were staggering and the Soviet Union was in the throws of evacuating and re-establishing tank and other military production at plants beyond the Ural mountains and the availability of any tank type on the front line was of critical importance to the Red Army. The T-60 story is that of a tank entering service at a time when the Soviet Union was in a war for its very survival, and the nearly 6000 T-60 tanks produced from the autumn of 1941 until the summer of 1942 were essential tools in that very struggle for survival.

---

*Taktika Tankovikh Voisk (Tactics of Tank Troops). T.P. Kuznetsov. Voenizdat, Moscow, 1940, pp11-12.

Chapter 1

Development History

The launch of Operation "Barbarossa" on 22nd June 1941 and subsequent Soviet fight for survival led to an immediate change in priorities for the Soviet tank industry. On 25th June 1941 a resolution issued by the Council of People's Commissars of the Soviet Union (SNK USSR) cancelled further development of several perspective tank and armoured vehicle designs, and also curtailed the production of several armoured vehicle types at the time already in series production, but which were considered too complex to mass produce under wartime conditions. The absolute priority was now concentration on the production of tried and tested current generation tanks and armoured vehicles. The decision affected many plants, including Plant №37 of the obliquely named Ministry of Medium Machine Building (NKSM) - which was actually responsible for tank production. Plant №37 in Moscow was ordered to by 1st August cease production of the amphibious T-40 reconnaissance tank and the semi-armoured

T-20 Komsomolets light artillery tractor then being built at the plant, in order to re-tool for the production of the new, heavier and non-amphibious T-50 light developed by Plant №174 (Leningrad). Plant №37 was expected to re-tool for the assembly of the new T-50 light tank within two months, with hull and turret sets to be provided by the nearby Ordzhonikidze plant in Podolsk, and other components for the T-50 to be provided by some 50 different plants located in Moscow and the surrounding region.

The decision to replace the amphibious T-40 small tank with the much better armed and armoured T-50 light tank was in principle entirely logical in that amphibious reconnaissance tanks were built in relatively small numbers, but were by the end of the 1930s in most circumstances not significantly more useful than wheeled armoured cars such as the BA-10 and new BA-11. The T-50 was meantime planned for major series production as a replacement for the T-26 light tanks series, and

A T-40 from the first Establishment Lot during military acceptance trials, 1940. (RGVA)

at the time fell within the state remit to concentrate on the series production of a smaller range of tank types. The plan to replace the T-26 light tank with the T-50 and to have plants such as Plant №37 move from T-40 to T-50 production would however prove fatally flawed, in that the T-50 featured many new and as yet unproven mechanical components. The heavier T-50 tank would prove so complex to manufacture that it would be prematurely removed from service, and the less complex T-60 would emerge as the ultimate successor to the T-40.

The T-40 had been adopted for service with the Red Army in December 1939, but had only briefly provided amphibious light tanks with an advantage over light wheeled armoured vehicles. Meantime the GAZ plant in Gorky had in 1939 begun development of the LB-62 armoured car, which had all-terrain performance comparable with the T-40 tank, with which it shared the same turret and 12.7mm DShK main armament. The LB-62 was by the summer of 1941 close to being adopted for service by the Red Army. With a potential production output greater than the T-40 then in production at Plant №37, the Red Army would now have a wheeled armoured car alternative to the T-40 tank, with similar firepower and armour, but greatly reduced maintenance requirements.

With regard to the potential replacement of the T-40 with the heavier and non-amphibious T-50, the latter tank with its 45mm M-1932/38 (20K) tank gun and heavier armour was clearly a much more powerful tank than the T-40 with its 12.7mm DShK armament and maximum 13mm armour thickness, while the lack of amphibious capability was not considered a critical factor. The T-50 was planned to be produced on a massive scale, initially at Plant №174 located in Leningrad, and additionally at Plant №37 in Moscow and Plant №172 in Omsk, such that it would not only entirely replace the T-26 light tank series but become one of the principle tanks of the Red Army in the 1940s. The T-50 was however an entirely more revolutionary design than the T-26. Though identically armed, it was much more heavily armoured and was powered by a new V-4 diesel engine coupled to an 8-speed planetary transmission, its relative complexity leading to significant delays in the start-up of production. The result was that the T-50 entered series production at Plant №174 in Leningrad in June 1941 just as the country was plunged into war.

During the first weeks after the commencement of "Operation Barbarossa" the belated start of T-50 series production was initially expected to fulfill a critical role in replacing the catastrophic losses of Red Army tanks in the initial weeks of conflict. However, Plant №174 suffered significant problems with establishing series manufacture (a problem which also affected the first series production T-34 medium tanks), in part due to the significantly thicker armour used on the T-50, with output

Trials of the LB-62 armoured car, summer 1941, Gorky area. In the background is a T-40 amphibious tank. (GAZ archive).

consequently slow and severely behind schedule. Plant №174 did at least have prior experience with heavier armour plate. Plant №37 by comparison had experience only of light artillery tractors and amphibious scout tanks, with standard automotive components extensively employed in their assembly, and all with a combat weight under 6 metric tonnes. It was therefore even less prepared than Plant №174 to tackle production of the T-50 "light" tank with a 14 metric tonne combat weight.

An additional, and acute, problem with the T-50 was its use of the new 6 cylinder V-4 diesel engine (one half of the V-2 used in the T-34) produced at Plant №75 NKSM in Kharkov, which was primarily tasked with production of V-2 engines for the T-34. Plant №75 had severe problems assembling the new engine, as a result of which production of the new and sophisticated T-50 at Plant №174 was almost at a standstill in July 1941, while Plant №75 had no choice but to cannibalize V-4 engine components for use in the V-2 engine produced at the same plant for the T-34, which was of higher strategic priority.

Had Plant №37 conformed to the letter with the 25th June 1941 resolution that demanded that it focus all efforts on developing the T-50 for series production, it is likely that production output of any tank types would have stalled entirely at the exact time tank output was most critical. The design bureau (KB) at Plant №37 headed by Nikolai Alexandrovich Astrov was however well aware of the formidable technical issues facing the plant in trying to establish series production of a significantly heavier tank type. Assembly of the 14 metric tonne T-50 would require major re-tooling of the assembly facilities, while the main assembly workshop did not even have overhead cranes capable of lifting the heavier component pieces. Plant №37 did not formally reject its obligation to establish T-50 production, and in fact even developed an amphibious T-135 variant on the base chassis (the 135 index was also used for the standard T-50). However, as a plant initiative the plant KB had secretly developed a simplified version of the then current T-40 amphibious tank that would be easier to produce than the T-50 under wartime conditions while using existing plant facilities. In early July a letter signed by N. A. Astrov and V. P. Okunev (the military representative of Plant №37) and addressed directly to Stalin was delivered to the Kremlin. The letter candidly (and somewhat bravely all things considered) outlined the

inability of Plant № 37 to fulfill its obligations relative to T-50 series production, describing T-50 production at the plant as effectively unworkable. The letter proposed as an alternative to start production of the plant initiative "060" small tank based on the T-40, arguing that it could be produced in significantly larger quantities than the T-50 without the associated trauma of establishing T-50 production. Stalin read the letter that same evening, approved of the plan, and instructed the Deputy Chairman of the SNK USSR, V. A. Malyshev - who was also People's Commissar of Medium Machine Building (NKSM) - to visit Plant №37 and personally oversee the project. Malyshev arrived at the plant the very next morning. Having reviewed the proposals with the plant management he on 14th July wrote to Vyacheslav Molotov, Chairman of the Council of People's Commissars, recommending the new "060" tank as proposed by Plant №37, to be armed with the new 20mm TNSh automatic cannon on which Astrov's design bureau had already been working in combination with OKB-15.

Three days later, on 17th July 1941 GKO Decree №179ss was issued *"On the production of T-60 light tanks at Plant №37*

Loading of T-40 (T-30) tanks, 42nd Tank Brigade, September 1941 (RGAKFD)

But for the outbreak of war, a new generation of wheeled armoured cars such as the LB-62, with the same turret and armament as the T-40, would have taken over the role of reconnaissance tanks in the Red Army. (GAZ plant archive)

Narkomsredmash (NKSM)", giving the go-ahead to develop the T-60 as a series production tank. The idea of T-50 production at Plant №37 was quietly dropped, although some attempts were made to return to the theme in the autumn of 1941.

Preparation for T-60 Series Production

With the T-60 (as it would later be definitively called) officially sanctioned for development as a series production tank, focus at State level now turned to rolling out T-60 production at several plants capable of assembling such a tank, including the KhTZ tractor plant in Kharkov and the GAZ automobile plant in Gorky, which would be required to assemble T-60 tanks using hull and turret sets delivered to the plants and fitted out with automotive and other components delivered to (or where possible manufactured directly within) the plants concerned.

In early Plant №37 internal correspondence the T-60 as it was later known was often conflated with the tank "030", which was the index initially used for the T-30, the 20mm ShVAK armed, better armoured but non-amphibious version of the T-40. The entirely new tank would ultimately receive the separate index "060", and would become the T-60 when accepted for service with the Red Army.

The decision to series produce the "060" (i.e. the T-60 rather than the T-30) was not without its own difficulties. The hull and turret of the earlier T-40 as produced at the Ordzhonikidze plant in Podolsk for T-40 assembly at Plant №37 was

relatively complex in design. The hull featured many acutely shaped armoured plates, the welding together of which was time consuming, while the turrets were assembled entirely from untreated armour plate. One of the major causes of early production disruption was the high scrap rate of hull and turret armour components, while the transition to the use of rolled homogeneous armour (RHA) plate in mid July 1941 only partially alleviated the problems associated with armour production. The move to a new and simpler tank design would ultimately simplify manufacturing and thereby reduce assembly times, but would take time to develop and implement.

On 20th July 1941, GKO Resolution №222ss was issued, which expanded the number of plants to be involved in T-60 production beyond Plant №37, to now include GAZ (Gorky) and KhTZ (Kharkov), with Plant №264 (Krasnoarmeisk - near Stalingrad) Plant №176 (Murom) and KPZ (Kolomna) and other plants to be involved in the assembly of hull and turret sets. The Podolsk plant - NKSM and Kolomensky plant - NKTP would supply Plant №37, Plant №176 (Murom), Plant №177 (Vyksa) and the Novo-Kramatorsky plant would supply GAZ, and the Krasny Kotelshchik and Voroshilovgradsky plants NKSM would supply KhTZ. Plant №264 was ultimately not accepted for hull assembly. GKO Resolution №222ss defined the obligations of the T-60 assembly plants and their respective component and sub-assembly suppliers. In part, the Resolution confirmed the following obligations:

GKO Resolution № 222ss, issued on 20th July 1941

"1. To oblige NKSM Comrade Malyshev to organize in plants: №37, KhTZ and GAZ in the 3rd and 4th quarters of this year, the production of 10,000 T-60 tanks, according to the specifications approved by GKO-179ss dated 17th July 1941, and according to the following schedule:

Assembly Plant	August	September	October	November	December
Plant № 37	200	650	850	900	900
KhTZ	50	500	950	1000	1000
GAZ	50	300	650	1000	1000
Total	300	1450	2450	2900	2900

2. To oblige Narkomneft (Ministry of Oil) - comrade Sedin, NKSM - comrade Kazakov, NKPS - comrade Kaganovich, NKChM - comrade Tevosyan and NKSP - comrade Nosenko to organize the production of the T-60 hull and turret sets for NKSM plants and ensure their delivery according to the following schedule:

Plant №37	July	August	September	October	November	December
Podolsk Plant NKTP	25	250	575	650	650	650
Kolomensky Plant NKTM (KPZ)	–	25	100	200	250	250

KhTZ Plant	–	August	September	October	November	December
Krasny Kotelshchik Plant NKTM	–	50	400	650	650	650
Voroshilovgradsky Plant NKTM	–	50	200	399	350	350

GAZ Plant	–	August	September	October	November	December
Vysunsky DRO Plant NKSS	–	250	575	650	650	650
Murom Plant NKPS	–	25	100	200	250	250
Novo-Kramatorsky Plant NKTM	–	25	75	175	350	350

The Kulebaksky plant NKSP heat treatment is to produce small armoured parts for DRO, and the Vyksa (Vyksunsky) steel works is engaged for heat treatment and billet parts.

3. To oblige NKChM – comrade Tevosyan and NKSP - comrade Nosenko to produce and deliver to the (assembly) plants: Podolsk, Krasny Kotelshchik (Taganrog), Vyksunsky DRO (Vyksa), Murom locomotive repair plant, (Kolomna), Voroshilovgradsky and Novo-Kramatorsky - 20,000 tonnes of steel plate "IZ" within given deadlines, ensuring compliance with the schedule of hull and turret set production. NKChM is to deliver 15,000 tonnes and NKSP - 5,000 tonnes of steel armour plate.

4. Allow NKChM and NKSP dispensation to make armour plate at the expense of a corresponding reduction in carbon steel.

5. Allow NKChM and NKSP to produce for the production of armour plate:

	NKChM	NKSP
Ferromolybdenum	75 tonnes	25 tonnes
75% ferrosilicon	375 tonnes	125 tonnes

6. Allow plants producing the hull (and turret) sets, to weld the casings without machining the edges of the armour plates.

7. To oblige NKSM – comrade Malyshev, Narkomneft, Sedin – to within 3 days provide manufacturers the hull and turret set working drawings, technology and technical data, and also to provide the plants all necessary technical assistance.

8. *To instruct NKO (GABTU KA) together with NKSP, NKChM and NKSM to within 2 days approve the technical conditions for the wartime production of armour plate and armoured parts for T-60 tanks and technical specifications for the production of these tanks, providing maximum simplification of the manufacture of both tanks and armour, while reducing spare parts requirements. To allow for hull manufacture without the requirement to bend-form the armour plate.*

9. *To oblige Narkomkhoz of the RSFSR (the Russian Federation within the Soviet Union) - comrade Makarov to allocate to NKSM on behalf of Plant №37 an assembly area at the Moscow "Svara" plant for the organization of T-60 assembly.*

10. *To oblige NKOM - comrade Parshin, NKTM - comrade Kazakov, Narkomneft - comrade Sedin, NKPS - comrade Kaganovich, NKEhP - comrade Bogatyrev, Narcomugol (Ministry of Coal) - comrade Vakhrushev, NKTS - comrade Efremov, NKAP - comrade Shakhurin to ensure the supply of Plant №37, KhTZ and GAZ components and parts tanks T-60 in the quantities and timescale required by this resolution.*

11. *To oblige Narkomresinprom - comrade Mitrokhin to provide rims for 90000 lower (i.e. roadwheels) and 60000 upper rollers(i.e. return rollers) for the T-60 within the timescale required by this resolution.*

12. *To oblige NKO (GABTU KA) to instruct NKV - comrade Ustinov to manufacture the required weapons and optics for T-60 tank production at plants: №37, KhTZ and GAZ in quantities and in accordance with the timescale required by this resolution.*

NKSM Resolution №360ss followed on 23rd July, whereby the design Bureau of Plant №37 was ordered to develop a simplified hull and turret design for the forthcoming T-60, to be developed at Plant №37 on the basis of the T-40, with series production to be initially undertaken at KhTZ and GAZ.

The simplifications required to modify the T-40 hull and turret arrangements into the effectively entirely new T-60 hull and turret set were agreed over a two-day technical meeting. Modifications included a 150mm reduction in overall hull height, simplification of the front and rear armour, elimination of the rear propeller tunnel, and simplification of the air intake arrangements. Rolled homogeneous (RHA) armour was to be used throughout, with increased armour protection, both in terms of thickness and armour inclination in some areas. The turret was to be of a new and simplified construction that avoided the need to bend, form and chamfer steel plate as required for the T-30/T-40 conical turret. A myriad of detail changes were also agreed, such that for-instance the fuel tanks were now to be hermetically sealed. There followed a long list of assemblies and components, specifying everything from the engine installation to the material to be used for the fuel pipes, the required tools and their ZIP (spare parts storage) boxes, to the type of seats required for the driver-mechanic and commander, all of which were (with exceptions allowed where maintaining production required it) to be interchangeable between the production plants. Further instructions included the following paragraphs, which have some relevance to the overall thinking behind the standardization of wartime T-60 production:

3) *Given the requirement to quickly master the mass production of tanks at the GAZ and KhTZ plants, the use of non-interchangeable components is allowed, the vast majority of which will not require replacement between capital repairs.*

4) *In order to provide tank troops with the correct spare parts, it is mandatory that:*

   a) *Tanks produced by GAZ and KhTZ, are designated T-70.*

   b) *Plant №37 is obliged by 1st September 1941 to develop a detailed spares catalogue for the T-40, T-60 and T-70, indicating parts interchangeability.*

5) *In connection with the large number of tanks ordered in the second half of 1941 - to reduce the amount of command tanks with radio installed to 20% instead of 40% (one tank in five to be equipped with radio).*

6) *Replace the standard tarpaulin with a (smaller) sheet of the same material limited to 6m2, giving the ability to transport it directly on the tank when not required.*

7) *To acknowledge the requirement to by the end of 1941 produce the T-60 developed at Plant №37 to the same specifications at both KhTZ and GAZ.*

The final paragraph (7) was reinforced in that it was also made mandatory that the parts manufactured at Plant №37, KhTZ and GAZ were to be interchangeable, an issue that had plagued T-34 field maintenance as it began to be series produced at several plants. This contradicted paragraph (3) but the intent was that parts should either be fit for total life of service, or interchangeable.

The T-60 was in effect far from a simplified non-amphibious version of the T-40. Plant №37 had in fact developed a new tank for production at Plant №37, KhTZ and GAZ, that differed significantly from the earlier design but was significantly more appropriate for series wartime production on a massive scale.

In order to avoid production disruption as the T-60 was readied for series production, and also not in small part due to a large available backlog of T-40 hull and turret sets being located at the Ordzhonikidze armour plant in nearby Podolsk,

A T-40 with an experimental 20mm ShVAK installation, August 1941 (TsAMO)

the decision was taken to continue production of the T-40 at Plant №37 until the end of 1941. The Ordzhonikidze armour plant in nearby Podolsk was not in a position to immediately switch production to T-60 hull and turret assembly due to other ongoing priorities, including manufacturing the armoured cockpits for the Il-2 "Shturmovik" ground attack aircraft. Further developments at Plant №37 led to the emergence of the non-amphibious "030" variant of the T-40, which was first designated T-30 at end of July 1941.

The modified "060" tank intended for production at KhTZ (Kharkov) and GAZ (Gorky) had now received the formal plant index "060" and was thereafter differentiated in production plant documentation from the "030" (T-30), which was the non-amphibious version of the T-40 armed with a 20mm TNSh (ShVAK) cannon, with the T-30 index being used from the end of July 1941. The prototype "060" began to be known as the production T-60 by the early autumn of 1941, and sometimes as T-60Sh (i.e. T-60 with 20mm ShVAK cannon armament), but even in 1942 the T-60 was still sometimes referred to in internal plant correspondence as the T-60M or even as the T-70 - which would latterly emerge as an entirely new tank design. It is noteworthy that the "030" and "060" tanks were both adopted for service with the Red Army (as the T-30 and T-60 respectively) before either prototype had been built and te-

sted, which reflected the urgency of the situation at the front. With the "030" the design risk was minimal, as the tank was effectively a simplified T-40 with increased armour and new armament, the design drawings for which took only two days to complete. The "060" by contrast differed significantly from its predecessor. Development work on the hull and turret of the simplified "060" design began on 20th July 1941, one month after the outbreak of war, with formal approval to commence actually being issued three days later, on 23rd July. The plant KB headed by Astrov may have set a world speed record for designing a tank: the drawings were completed on 27th July, i.e. the entire design project was completed in a week, as confirmed by the dates on the original plant drawings.

Engine Options

The "060" was effectively a simplified version of the earlier T-40, albeit with significant changes to the armour layout, automotive components and main armament. One of the design advantages of the T-40, and the later T-30 and T-60, was the ability to assemble these "small" tanks in facilities other than tank plants, with minimum specialist tooling, and using standard automotive components. GAZ would soon become one of the major T-60 production facilities, and the default engine supplier for other plants; however this never entirely stable arrangement was some time in the making. In October 1940, control of the engine production workshops at the GAZ Molotov Plant was handed to the People's Commissariat of Aviation Industry (NKAP) in order that the engine workshops at the vehicle plant concentrate on production of the M-105 aviation engine. At the time the workshops were producing the GAZ-11 and GAZ-202 automotive engines, the GAZ-11 engine being used in T-40 production at Plant №37 and also being the designated engine for a whole series of new GAZ vehicles, on which work would now have to be terminated.

With future GAZ vehicle engine production now in doubt, alternative engine installations were required for the T-40, and in late November 1940, the idea of installing the ZiS-16 engine, (an uprated version of the ZiS-5 engine from the ZiS-5 3 tonne truck; with a power output of 85hp) was considered, together with a diesel variant, the D-7. A T-40 tank was delivered to ZiS for installation and evaluation of the potential new engines, but installing any of the alternative ZiS engines in the existing T-40 tank proved impossible without increasing the size of the engine compartment.

By June 1941, problems with the supply of GAZ-202 engines had been long resolved; however when designing the T-60, and the engine compartment in particular, the head of Department 22 responsible for hull design, A. V. Bogachev, took into consideration the pre-war engine supply difficulties. Despite the hull of the T-60 being 150mm lower than that of the T-40, the layout of the ancillary components in the engine compartment was arranged in such a way that the standard GAZ-202 engine could if required be replaced by ZiS-5 or uprated ZiS-16 engines, or the D-7 diesel variant, so that lack of any given engine supplier would not entirely shut down tank production output. Some months later, when supply difficulties were problematical during the darkest months of the war, this would prove to be a wise decision, and a recurring theme.

Overhead view of the 20mm ShVAK installed in a T-40, August 1941. The T-60 installation was identical. (TsAMO)

Armament Options

The "030" and "060" were originally planned to retain the 12.7mm DShK and co-axial 7.62mm DT armament combination from the T-40, the installation of a 20mm cannon as main armament being partly due to supply problems with the 12.7mm DShK rather than any concern for the effectiveness of the smaller calibre weapon. The plants involved in DShK production (in particular Plant №507 NKV located in Lopasnya south of Moscow (today Chekhov) could produce only a few hundred DShK guns per month. On 23rd July 1941 Marshal G. I. Kulik, the Deputy People's Commissar of Defense, not necessarily known for his bright decisions on tank armament, held an urgent meeting to review upgrading the armament on the new T-60, and on this occasion came to an effective conclusion, particularly considering that DShK production was not expected to ease in the near future.

The 20mm ShVAK (TNSh) cannon with which the T-60 was ultimately armed, was developed in 1936 by OKB-15 NKV as a large-calibre automatic aviation cannon, provided with armour-piercing ammunition. It became the first series production weapon of its type in the Soviet Union, and by the beginning of the "Great Patriotic War" the 20mm ShVAK was a standard installation in fighter aircraft and the Il-2 "Shturmovik" ground attack aircraft. The 20mm ShVAK would in 1941 be adapted for tank use, and was to become the default armament on the production T-60, but there were previous attempts to re-arm the earlier T-40 series which had a bearing on the armament ultimately selected for the T-60.

In 1940, the 23-mm PT-23TB automatic cannon (a tank version of the 23mm MP-6) was developed at OKB-16 under the leadership of Ya. G. Taubin for potential use on the T-40 and subsequent tanks. Development proved problematical however, with the test firing scheduled for January 1941 being cancelled, and a worn MP-6 being sent for test firing in lieu of the PT-23B. Some time later, and days before the ultimate start of testing, the PT-23TB gun was removed from the T-40 in which it was then installed and re-fitted on the experimental TsAKB-50 armoured aerosan. While these events were unfolding, Taubin maintained that the MP-6 was in series production, which clearly was not the case. In May, the military ran out of patience, Taubin and his deputy M. N. Baburin were arrested, and the subject of arming the T-40 with the 23mm

A T-50 light tank during firing trials, ANIOP polygon, early June 1941. (TsAMO)

PT-23TB was dropped. As an alternative, it was proposed to mount the similar 23-mm VYa-23 automatic cannon, originally developed for aircraft use at OKB-14 under the command of A. A. Volkov and S. A. Yartsev. Plans to mount the 23mm VYa-23 in a tank installation were however frustrated by the weapon's excessive recoil considering the relatively small turret in which it would be installed. The weapon was as of May 1941 also not yet in series production, so represented a development risk. In the circumstances, the decision was taken to install a tank version of the relatively tried and tested 20mm ShVAK automatic aircraft cannon on forthcoming small tanks, which would materialize on the T-30 and T-60.

The decision to mount the 20mm ShVAK in the T-60 was formalized by GKO Resolution №289ss "About the armament of the T-60" issued on 26th July 1941, in accordance with which the T-60 was officially to be armed with the 20-mm ShVAK developed by OKB-15. The ShVAK would receive the index ShVAK TNSh / M-1941 only later, in September 1941, with the weapon subsequently being referred to by both its original ShVAK (aviation) and later TNSh (tank) version designations.

Resolution №289ss defined the requirements for prototype testing and series production for installation in Red Army small tanks, stating (in part) that:

"1. In addition to the GKO Committee Resolution (№222ss) dated 20th July 1941, to approve for the T-60 the following weapons:

a) 20mm calibre ShVAK machine gun and co-axial DT.

b) ammunition complement - 750 rounds for the ShVAK and 950 rounds for the DT.

2. To obligate NKSM (comrade Malyshev) and Plant №37 (comrade Levitansky) to by 6th August 1941 install the ShVAK gun in the turret of a T-60 and submit to NKO for testing.

3. To obligate NKO (comrades Kulik and Fedorenko) to within three days test the ShVAK installation in the T-60 and provide its conclusions.

4. To obligate NKSM (comrade Malyshev), Plant №37 (comrade Levitansky), Kharkov Tractor Plant (KhTZ) (comrade Parfenov) and the Molotov Automobile Plant (GAZ) (comrade Loskutov) to from 15th August to begin production of T-60 tanks armed with the DShK and DT."

The resolutions issued in late July were clear; but at the time the prototype TNSh tank version of the ShVAK was still under development. The first test article was mounted in a T-40 tank (Serial №11726) for trials purposes and submitted for firing trials from 7th to 10th August 1941.

In developing the 20mm TNSh (as the tank version would subsequently become known) parts were taken from both the aircraft wing and turret versions of the ShVAK, with minimal

This is the first prototype "060" fitted with a T-30 conical turret. The prototype was used by the GAZ "Molotov" plant as a test-mule and for training purposes. (GAZ)

This Russian drawing from a training manual shows some of the distinctive features of the T-60. The octagonal turret with its 20mm TNSh armament is evident, as is the use of cast spoked road wheels common on some T-60 production variants.

rework required. On the first prototype T-60, the TMPF sight remained unchanged from that of the DShK and DT installation co-axial combination as used on the T-40 and planned for the early T-60. The second prototype T-60 (armed with the 20mm ShVAK / TNSh) used a modified TMPF-1 sight. One significant change was that while the 12.7mm DShK was fed from a continuous belt, the 20mm TNSh was fed via 58-60 round capacity box magazines.

The 20mm ShVAK / TNSh had similar armour penetration to the 12.7mm DShK but with that penetration extended out to a greater range. The weapon was sighted to a theoretical maximum 2500m direct fire range, and 7000m for indirect fire. The weapon had a burst rate of fire of 750 rounds/minute and the "Br" armour-piercing rounds with a muzzle velocity of 815m/s could penetrate up to 35mm of vertical armour at close range. The tank could thereby easily destroy most secondary armoured vehicles at range, and the PzKpfw III and PzKpfw IV were vulnerable at short range, particularly on the side armour. The T-60 was provided with an ammunition complement of 13 boxes of 20mm ammunition each containing 58-60 rounds. The co-axial 7.62mm DT machine gun was provided with a 1008 round ammunition complement (16 discs).

The 20mm TNSh armament of the T-60 was then an entirely adequate weapon for its intended role at the time it was introduced into service on the T-60 tank. Perhaps of more immediate importance that the ordnance characteristics, installation of the 20mm ShVAK / TNSh in the T-60 in lieu of the 12.7mm DShK also addressed the problem of DShK production output lagging far behind the exponentially increased demand, albeit the 12.7mm DShK could also have been assembled at additional plants.

Meantime, on 30th July 1941 (i.e. before the weapon even began firing tests) the State Artillery Directorate (GAU) was presented with a list of demands related to production of the ShVAK, its optics and ammunition, with an initial requirement for 15 million rounds of 20mm ammunition for the new weapon. Only four days later, on 3rd August, the ammunition demand was modified, still with the same demand for 15 million rounds for delivery to the tank assembly plants, but now with an additional 35 million round contract for disbursal to the Red Army. The production plants meantime were not in a position to exponentially increase production, GAU confirming on 17th September that total output for the month would not exceed

30,000 rounds. The next day, following a direct intervention by the Deputy Chairman of the Council of People's Commissars of the Soviet Union L.Z. Mekhlis, the People's Commissar of Ammunition P. N. Goremykin modified the targets to 30,000 rounds for delivery to KhTZ, 20,000 rounds for GAZ and 50,000 rounds for Plant №37. The total production target for October was however set at an exponential 3.5 million rounds.

The 20mm ShVAK was built at Plant №2 (Kovrov) as was the later 20mm TNSh. The 20mm TNSh was also produced at Plant №535 (Tula), and in 1942 at Plant №314 and Plant №525; however the latter plants produced only 363 TNSh weapons in total.

Nikolai Aleksandrovich Astrov - T-60 Designer

The chief designer at Plant №37 in Moscow at the time the T-60 was conceived was Nikolai Aleksandrovich Astrov. Born in 1906, Astrov after graduation from the Moscow Electro-Machine Building Plant began his career working in industry, and after some time working on tractor designs had become involved in tank design with the experimental PT-1 and PT-1A amphibious tanks. He began work at Plant №37 in 1934 where, prior to working on the T-60, his earlier design projects that had entered series production included the T-38 and the T-40 amphibious light tanks and the T-20 Komsomolets light artillery tractor.

The T-60 was designed by Astrov at Plant №37 as a simplified version of the T-40 better suited for wartime mass produc-

An early production T-60 with conical turret, with a Voroshilovets tractor in the background. Red Square, Moscow, 7th November 1941. (O.Baronov)

tion, while the non-amphibious version of the T-40, the T-30 concurrently received the same 20mm TNSh armament as the newer T-60 design.

Subsequent to developing the T-60 for series production at several tank plants, Astrov and his design engineers were relocated to GAZ in Gorky as Plant №37 was evacuated from Moscow. Now located in Gorky, his engineers developed the GAZ-70, which in modified form would replace the T-60 in series production as the T-70, with the final variant of the series being the T-80. The same design team also developed the SU-76 self-propelled gun, which was second only to the T-34 in terms of total numbers produced.

In 1943, as the Red Army moved onto the offensive, many of Astrov's designers relocated back to Moscow, to Plant №40 (MMZ) in Mytischi in the northern suburbs of the city, with Astrov himself returning in 1945 and becoming chief of the OKB-40 design bureau in 1946. Post-war designs developed by Astrov at Plant №40 (renamed the Moscow Machine Building Plant - MMZ in 1948) included the ASU-57 and ASU-85 airborne self propelled guns, the ZSU-23-4 "Shilka" self propelled anti-aircraft system and the 2P25 tracked chassis for the "Kub" anti-aircraft missile (SAM) system, and in later years the chassis for its ultimate replacements, the "Buk" and "Tor". SAM systems, all alongside the building of metro trains which was and remains today the plant's main civilian activity. Astrov died in 1992 at the age of 86.

Nikolai Aleksandrovich Astrov. During his career Astrov designed 26 different armoured vehicles, including all the pre-war series production amphibious light tanks and wartime light tanks, the T-60 included. From 1934-1941 Astrov was the Chief Designer at Plant №37 where the T-60 design was developed. (IZ)

Mikhail Nikolaevich Shukin was the Chief Designer at Plant №38 in Kirov from 1942-44 having before evacuation to Kirov been Chief Designer at Kolomna Machine Building Plant (KMZ) where he also worked on the T-60 design.

The T-60 was assembled at several plants in a number of guises. This up-armoured T-60, assembled at Plant №37 after relocation to Sverdlovsk, has a mix of features including the distinctive Plant №37 (Sverdlovsk production) turret which gave marginally increased working space for the hard pressed commander/gunner/loader. This particular tank also has different roadwheel types. (RGAE)

Chapter 2

T-60 Production at Plant №37 (Moscow), KhTZ (Kharkov) & GAZ (Gorky)

In late July 1941, within a month of the Soviet Union being plunged into total war, the T-60 was being readied for series production, and production of the T-60, its armament and ammunition were now a matter of the assembly plants fulfilling their orders as defined by the State. However, as might be expected during the initial months of a war for survival, the reality at the assembly plants was very different from the paper requirements to fulfill production targets.

Plant №37 was expected to start production of the "030"* (T-30) from 1ˢᵗ August 1941, with production of the "060"* (T-60) meantime planned to begin at both KhTZ in Kharkov and GAZ in Gorky on 15ᵗʰ August. As with the armament and ammunition, there were inevitable delays in the start-up of T-60 series production, now under wartime conditions.

Of the steelworks expected to deliver "060" hull and turret sets to the assembly plants for August production, only the "Ordzhonikidze" plant in Podolsk managed to assemble a prototype hull on time, and that constructed of mild steel. Plant №2 (the "Kirkizh" Plant in Kovrov) managed to ship only 15 TNSh cannon in August, and Plant №69 (the "Lenin" Plant in Krasnogorsk, later famous for "Zenit" camera production) had delivered only 25 TMFP sights by mid-August. Final assembly of series production T-60 tanks was off to a slow start.

First Prototype "060"

Assembly of the first prototype "060" tank began at Plant №37 on 17ᵗʰ August 1941 under the direct supervision of N.A. Astrov. The prototype was fitted with a conical T-40 turret complete with mountings for its standard 12.7mm DShK and 7.62mm DT co-axial armament, aimed via a TMPF gunsight, though the armament and optics were not actually installed. The planned ammunition complement for the T-60 if fitted with the 12.7mm DShK was 500 rounds of (belt-fed) 12.7mm and 2016 rounds (32 discs) of 7.62mm ammunition, and 10 F-1 grenades. The first prototype "060" tank was assembled as a working model to familiarize other plants, specifically GAZ,

with the production nuances of the new tank type, with Astrov and Okunev travelling to Gorky to personally oversee the start of series production, before again returning to Plant №37 where the T-60 was originally designed.

In addition to using a T-40 turret, the first prototype was fitted with other at the time experimental components, including the cast road and idler wheels as would later become a feature of some production tanks. Development of these cast wheels with their distinctive spoked design which were simpler to produce while remaining adequately resilient for use on a light tank began in early August 1941 with a memorandum from Plant №37 to the Chief of the 3ʳᵈ Department BTU GABTU KA, military engineer 1ˢᵗ rank S. A. Afonin, dated 10ᵗʰ August, which explained the reasoning:

"The GKO task to produce the tanks "030" and "060" (at several plants) negates the possibility of fitting road wheels and idler wheels of welded construction on all tanks, as these can be series produced only at the GAZ plant, which does not have the production capacity to satisfy "030" and "060" production requirements at our plant (i.e. Plant №37), GAZ and KhTZ. As neither our plant nor KhTZ has equipment for the production of welded construction road wheels we must transition to another, less time-consuming production method which can be undertaken without the special equipment only available at GAZ, namely cast road wheels and idlers". The design of the cast road wheels and idlers is similar to that developed for the 400Kh76 (400X76 in the original Russian) wheels for the "Komsomolyets" tractor, which is entirely reliable and proven, while retaining interchangeability with welded construction wheels.

Although cast road wheels and idlers have not been fully tested on the "030" and "060" tanks, we consider that their reliability is not in doubt, as the structural elements have been dimensionally increased in accordance with the increased load. The increase in overall tank weight using these rollers is 26kg. We request approval of our design drawings for the road wheels (030-07-008) and idlers (010-07-031). These wheels are interchangeable with the welded type in series production".

---

* Plant №37 in Moscow used the index "010" for tank projects, hence "030", "060", etc. This was carried over to prototypes developed at Plant №37 after relocation to Sverdlovsk, hence projects "061", "062", "063" etc. The later T-70 was developed at GAZ to where the Astrov KB had relocated from Plant №37 in Moscow. Consequently, although the T-70 prototype is sometimes described as "070", the tank was designated GAZ-70 within GAZ and the "070" is a misnomer.

The KhTZ-16 armoured tractor was built at KhTZ as an interim measure as the plant prepared for T-60 assembly. At the time the T-60 was being prepared for series production, the KhTZ plant was under immediate threat of capture, and there were in consequence internal conflicts at the plant as to whether to continue KhTZ-16 production or belatedly start T-60 production with the enemy almost literally at the gates.

Although cast road wheels and idlers were developed at Plant №37 in Moscow, and series production started there in October, they were not used on the T-30 tanks assembled at Plant №37, as the plant had sufficient inventory of forged and welded wheels to satisfy all T-30 production before it was evacuated to Sverdlovsk. Nor were these cast wheels fitted to T-60 tanks assembled by the KhTZ plant, as there was simply no time to put them into series production for reasons outlined below. Some T-60 tanks produced by GAZ at the end of 1941 were fitted with cast road wheels, produced by STZ in Stalingrad, though the number of such tanks assembled at GAZ was small.

Second Prototype "060"

The second prototype "060" was assembled at Plant №37 in September 1941, now armed with the 20mm TNSh L/82.4 automatic cannon developed at the OKB-15 design bureau in collaboration with OKB-16 on the basis of the ShVAK aircraft cannon, and with a slightly modified TMFP-1 gunsight. The secondary armament remained unchanged; however the ammunition complement was modified to accommodate the larger size of the 20mm rounds, the tank now being stowed with 745 rounds of 20mm (13 box magazines) and only 945

rounds of 7.62mm (15 discs). Stalin personally attended the foreshortened plant trials of the second T-60 prototype, which was effectively a modified variant of the first prototype, armed with the 20mm TNSh as originally envisaged for the T-60.

T-60 Production at Plant №37 (Moscow)

Plant №37, also known as the Ordzhonikidze plant, was from 1931 assigned with the task of producing "small" tanks for the Red Army, which in accordance with Red army tables was any tank with a combat weight under 6 metric tonnes and with machine gun main armament. The plant built the T-27 tankette, the T-37A, the T-38 and also the Pioner and Komsomolets light artillery tractors. These tanks and artillery tractors were powered by standard GAZ-AA and GAZ-M automotive engines and were fitted with other standard automobile components including transmissions and differentials. The task of assembling the T-60 was therefore only an issue of manufacturing the armoured hull and turret sets at specialized armour plants with the facilities to produce, treat and assemble armoured steel plate.

Plant №37 completed its first T-60 on 15th September 1941; and was well advanced with plans to manufacture the

T-60 in place of the T-30 however on 9th October 1941 the plant received orders to evacuate the plant machine tooling and personnel to safety beyond the Ural Mountains. Russian sources are conflated regarding series production at Plant №37 at its original Moscow location, but it would seem that the T-60 was assembled at Plant №37 until 26th October 1941, at which time some 245 T-60 tanks had been assembled at Plant №37 in Moscow, a number of which may have in fact been T-30 tanks delivered as T-60s. T-60 production resumed at Plant №37, now relocated to Sverdlovsk, in December 1941.

T-60 Production at KhTZ (Kharkov)

The situation at the Kharkov Tractor Plant (KhTZ), which was intended to become a major producer of the T-60, was in the summer of 1941 not particularly conducive to starting series production of a new tank type. Within literally days after the outbreak of war, the plant KB had in early July 1941 developed the KhTZ-16 armoured tractor as a plant initiative to start armoured vehicle production, based on the heavily modified chassis of the SKhTZ-NATI tracked agricultural tractor. On 20th July 1941, even before the prototype of the KhTZ-16 was completed, GKO Resolution №219ss was issued, instructing KhTZ plant to manufacture 2000 of the hybrid armoured

As the KhTZ plant in Kharkov was over-run by Axis forces in September 1941, few photographic records of T-60 production there have survived. This is an external view of the assembly workshop, now under Wehrmacht control.

tractors. GABTU perfectly understood that such assembly was an interim measure, and that the KhTZ-16 was not a fully-fledged fighting vehicle; however it was a temporary solution using locally available chassis and components. Trials confirmed that speed, range and overall mobility were limited as expected; while the casemate mounted 45mm tank gun had a limited arc of fire. For good measure the KhTZ-16's engine also severely overheated during trials. Nevertheless, the SKhTZ-NATI chassis was readily available, and gave the KhTZ tractor plant the ability to master "tank" production on the agricultural tractor chassis.

Clearly understanding the limited combat effectiveness and temporary nature of the KhTZ-16, GABTU, on the same day as GKO Resolution №219ss on the KhTZ-16 was issued, also issued GKO Resolution №222ss. The latter instructed KhTZ to, in parallel with KhTZ-16 production, prepare for series production of the T-60 at the KhTZ plant. The production start date and output requirements specified in the latter resolution would, however, prove entirely unrealistic.

Meantime, the "060" technical documentation began to be dispatched from the KB at Plant №37, the first drawings arriving at KhTZ on 28th July, with the bulk of the documentation arriving only on 10th August. As of 16th August the plant had not received documentation on the T-60 acceptance test parameters, and there was no instruction on spare parts provisions. While waiting for the "delayed" drawings (inconsequential in peacetime, but critical in July 1941 considering Kharkov's location) the KhTZ plant made logistical preparations for T-60 series production. A joint meeting between the management of KhTZ and KhEMZ (the Kharkov Electromechanical plant) was held on 8th August to determine the respective allocation of parts production between the plants.

The main supply problem at KhTZ in Kharkov was the delivery of hull and turret sets. Turret manufacture was delayed at KhTZ due to the need to redesign the turret for installation of the 20mm TNSh automatic gun, with the assembly drawings being available to the production plants only at the end of August. The hull fabricators were meantime loaded with other and equally critical work, such that the planned production start-up of T-60 in August 1941 proved to be impossible. The first prototype "060" hull destined for KhTZ final assembly was built at the "October Revolution" plant in Voroshilovgrad only at the end of August, by which time series production at KhTZ should have been well advanced.

The KhTZ plant also had manpower shortages due to workers being drafted into the Red Army, with only six engineers assigned to the task of T-60 production start-up in Kharkov in mid August. There were also understandable difficulties in that KhTZ expertise was in tracked tractor rather than tank production. The drawings provided by Plant №37 had to be rewor-

A T-60 in the typical configuration as delivered by GAZ from October 1941 through the winter of 1941-42. (TsAMO)

Frontal view of a GAZ production T-60. Note the lack of details such as driving lights.

ked for local production purposes, which also took time, with some minor parts being "borrowed" from the KhTZ-16 armoured tractor as they were readily available and the specified components were not. T-60 production at KhTZ nevertheless seems to have taken second priority to the "in house" KhTZ-16 armoured tractor. The situation at KhTZ is described in a Memorandum dated 1ˢᵗ September 1941, sent by the GABTU military representative at KhTZ, Military Engineer 2ⁿᵈ Rank Plakhov, to the People's Commissariat of State Control, relating to certain components but indicative of the situation at KhTZ in general:

"Despite repeated reminders and warnings, KhEMZ has not delivered the required side friction clutches. Only on 27ᵗʰ August 1941 the director of KhEMZ comrade Skidarenko advised representatives of BTU and KhTZ that "I have not made any side friction clutches and will not make them", explaining that this was due to both a lack of grinding machines for the manufacture of the required discs and having recently received permission from the People's Commissar of Electrical Industry and from NKSM - comrade Malyshev - to terminate the KhTZ order. KhTZ, having expected KhEMZ to produce these parts, has not arranged production within the plant. KhEMZ, has in turn not manufactured even a single set, nor did it advise KhTZ to make alternative arrangements. As a result, KhTZ gave this manufacturing work to its own

workshops only on 29ᵗʰ August 1941, when per the People's Commissariat schedule, series production of tanks should have started by 1ˢᵗ September and in accordance with GKO requirements, the KhTZ plant was to have delivered 50 (T-60) tanks by 1ˢᵗ September 1941.

I believe that the behavior of comrade Skidorenko at KhEMZ borders on the criminal. He did not notify KhTZ of his refusal to execute the order, as originally agreed, lost much time, did not start procuring the required production tooling, and left KhTZ with a lack of critical components required for the assembly of the first production (T-60) tanks.

The KhTGZ plant (the "Kirov" Turbo-generator Plant) in Kharkov also requires the same resolution to deliver roadwheels and idlers for KhTZ, which has to date received not a single set due to a lack of bending and welding equipment (at KhTGZ). KhEMZ, located under the same roof as KhTGZ, refuses to assist with the forming and welding of road wheels. Taking into account that before joining the assembly line the road wheels must be sent to Yaroslavl for the fitment of rubber rims, the delay in road wheel production wrecks the production delivery schedule.

It is additionally reported that to date the Voroshilovgrad plant and the "Krasny Kotelshchik" plant in Taganrog have not sent armoured hulls and other armoured parts for the T-60, the GAZ "Molotov" plant has not delivered engines (on 30ᵗʰ August 1941 a total of 7 engines were received at KhTZ, which were missing electrical equipment and carburetors); Plant №34 has not delivered radiators, and Glavkommezhprom and NKS have not supplied

Rear view of the same GAZ production tank.

The idler wheels on this GAZ production T-60 are standard 515mm diameter roadwheels rather than the design 460mm type. (TsAMO)

KhTZ and other Kharkov based sub-contractors with the necessary materials for increased production, in particular, no steel for the production of torsion bars. Please take all measures within your control." (Signed): Military Engineer 2nd Rank Plakhov.

The above letter gives some indication as to the difficulties being encountered by various production plants, with often-conflicting requirements. KhGTZ would ship the first 20 road wheels and idlers (sufficient for precisely two tanks) to Yaroslavl, some 1130km distant, for mounting of their rubber rims only two weeks later, on 12th September, for them to then be shipped back to KhTZ in Kharkov.

The situation at Kharkov was critical, not least because German and Axis forces were approaching Kiev (which would fall on the 21st September) and advance units were already close to Kharkov. Malyshev personally intervened in the problematical supply chain process, instructing Plant №37 to dispatch all the missing parts required to complete the first T-60 tanks at KhTZ. The foundry at KhTZ meantime began to produce cast road wheels in lieu of the original stamped, welded and rubber rimmed design, the first samples of which were ready by mid September. KhTZ also belatedly began to manufacture its own final drive components in lieu of those KhEMZ had failed to deliver, while Plant №183 supplied KhTZ with torsion bars as an interim solution.

While all these problems with T-60 components were being resolved, the plant management at KhTZ remained adamantly against phasing out production of the KhTZ-16 armou-

red tractor, eventually being forced to do so due to direct intervention from Malyshev. The reasoning, and some idea of the internal tensions within the plant, can be understood from the report of Military Engineer 3rd Rank Kulikov, senior engineer of the 3rd Department BTU KA dated the first half of September 1941:

"Parallel production of the KhTZ-16 and the T-60 is planned until the second half of September (17th September 1941), as the KhTZ-16 (chassis) can be produced on the main production line at the tractor assembly plant, and assembly of the T-60 can be arranged in another shop in an empty place, where a temporary production line has been prepared. After assembly the T-60 can be transferred to the main assembly line. Before the arrival of Malyshev the plant personnel were of a mind to remove the T-60 from production. But after he drove them hard, there was a noticeable change and the workshops began to pay more attention to assembly of the T-60. Before that the tank was so secret that none of the workers knew what they were going to manufacture at the plant."

The memorandum raises questions as to what exactly was going on at the plant. The lack of some critical parts for the new T-60 was understood, but despite the direct intervention of Malyshev, the release of many parts for the T-60 was hindered by a number of workshops continuing to work on components for the KhTZ-16 armoured tractor. Considering the strategic position of Kharkov at the time, with the enemy almost literally at the gates it is entirely likely that KhTZ plant management saw no sense in trying to start production of a new tank type

A T-60 undergoing final pre-delivery inspection at GAZ under the control of Sgt. G.A. Trusakov, 1942.

when the plant could continue to produce ersatz armoured tractors for which chassis, parts and armament were available.

The first T-60 was completed at KhTZ on 13th September, almost a month behind schedule. KhTZ had received its first two hull and turret sets from the "Krasny Kotelshchik" plant in Taganrog three days earlier, on 10th September 1941, and at the time the first tank was completed (from a hull and turret set from Voroshilovgrad) the plant had in total only 12 hull and turret sets available in inventory, provided from three different supply plants.

The T-60 ultimately entered series production at KhTZ too late to affect the war effort. By mid September German and other Axis forces were closing on Kharkov, and manufacturing plants in the city began to be evacuated, with preparations for the evacuation of KhTZ beginning on 17th September, precisely four days after the first T-60 was completed at the plant. For the month of September, KhTZ delivered 7 new T-60 tanks to the Red Army, which exactly matched the number of engines the plant had available for installation.

The KhTZ plant was still in the process of being evacuated to Stalingrad when on 24th October 1941 Kharkov was lost to the advancing German and Axis forces, which captured the KhTZ plant, much of its machine tooling and a number of

incomplete T-60s. For several months thereafter, the GAZ "Molotov" plant in Gorky would be the only manufacturer of T-60 tanks.

T-60 Production at GAZ (Gorky)

The Gorky "Molotov" Avtomobil Zavod (GAZ) had been an obvious choice for T-60 tank assembly. GAZ had supplied the GAZ-11 Model 202 engine (better known as the GAZ-202) for earlier T-40 production at Plant №37, together with the gearbox, torsion bars, forged solid disc road wheels and idlers, together with all the cast iron parts required for T-40 final assembly at Plant №37. GAZ also planned to launch the GAZ-22 artillery tractor at the plant using T-40 components; and elements of the T-40 tank including the turret with armament were also used at GAZ for development of the LB-62, series production of which was scheduled to start in the summer of 1941, so the plant already had significant armoured vehicle experience.

The situation at the GAZ plant was however in August 1941 not particularly different to that faced by KhTZ in Kharkov before the city was captured. The "late" delivery of production drawings to the hull and turret set fabricators had in turn delayed the delivery of hull and turret sets to the GAZ plant.

The Vyksa (Vyksunsky DRO) plant assembled the first T-60 hull prototype by the middle of August, with GABTU expecting series production to begin not earlier than 1ˢᵗ September. Meantime the GAZ plant had in August begun preparing for T-60 series production, with the plant KB modifying a significant portion of the production drawings to meet local specifics, as had also been done by the KB at KhTZ. Many design changes were made to the "standard " T-60 drawings as provided by Plant №37, with the GAZ KB designing its own fabricated items such as the track guard mounted ZIP (spare parts) boxes.

While one of the main problems at KhTZ in Kharkov had been the need to convert from agricultural tracked tractor to tank production (albeit with the hull and turret sets supplied from other plants) the main issue with introducing the T-60 into series production at GAZ was that the plant was a primary manufacturer of wheeled transport vehicles for the Red Army rather than a tank plant, and was already loaded to capacity with such production.

When in August 1941 the GAZ plant was tasked with preparing for series production of the T-60 tank, the plant was manufacturing a whole series of wheeled military vehicles. GAZ was the only Soviet plant producing 1.5 tonne capacity trucks (the GAZ-AA) desperately needed at the front, and had just started series production of the GAZ-64 reconnaissance vehicle, the GAZ-61 all-terrain command car and its GAZ-61-416 wheeled artillery tractor variant. The latter was developed on the GAZ-61 chassis in July as a wheeled replacement for T-20 Komsomolets tracked artillery tractor discontinued at Plant №37, and was also intended for towing light anti-tank guns. The GAZ-61 series was powered by the same 6 cylinder GAZ-11 engine as used in the T-40 and (as the GAZ-202) in the T-60. Production of these engines had been interrupted some months earlier by a conflicting demand to produce M-105 aviation engines in the same workshops, with GAZ-11 vehicle engine production having recovered to required levels only in the late summer of 1941 just before the new demands for T-60 production were introduced. GAZ at the time was also producing the MS-1 chassis for the BA-20 armoured car assembled at the Vyksa DRO plant, and the GAZ-07 chassis for the BA-10M armoured car assembled at the Izhorsk plant. Subsequent to GKO Resolution №222, GAZ was also tasked with production of a significant number of parts for small tanks, such that the plant was loaded with all manner of production for the Red Army.

On 21ˢᵗ August 1941 an agreement was nevertheless signed between GABTU and GAZ on the required T-60 production schedule. According to the NKSM approved plan GAZ was to deliver T-60 tanks in the final quarter of 1941 as follows:

	October 1941	November 1941	December 1941
T-60	170	280	360
T-60 with Radio	40	70	90

A typically configured GAZ production T-60. (TsAMO)

This overhead view of a GAZ production T-60 clearly shows the compact layout of the tank. (IsAMO)

An early GAZ production T-60 of the 33ʳᵈ Tank Brigade enters Red Square on 7ᵗʰ November 1941 for the annual, and last wartime, military parade on Red Square. The tank is fitted with the standard octagonal turret. The tanks embarked directly to the front line, only a few kilometres distant, after the parade. (RGAKFD)

The value of a standard T-60 line tank with armament, full ammunition complement and spare parts was determined at 81,000 Rubles, rising to 82,700 Rubles for command tanks fitted with a 71-TK-3 or 10-R radio set, it being interesting that the cost accounting was a factor during a time of national emergency.

On paper, GAZ was set to join KhTZ as the next (and as the situation deteriorated at KhTZ, the only) assembly plant to produce the T-60. However as at KhTZ there were at GAZ in September a myriad of technical and supply chain complications that delayed the production start up, which mirrored the problems faced by KhTZ during start-up operations there. The Murom Plant NKPS was to have completed its first four hull and turret sets for GAZ by mid September, but was unable to complete a single set for the whole month. The Novo-Kramatorsk plant NKTM had been tasked with completing 32 hull and turret sets by mid September, but had also not delivered a single set on schedule. The Vyksa DRO plant had been tasked to complete 6 hull and turret sets by the same date, and had indeed managed to deliver two sets, the first hull and turret set arriving at GAZ from Vyksa on 17ᵗʰ September. GAZ completed the first T-60 tank at workshop №5, dedicated to T-60 assembly, the very same day.

The armament for the T-60 was also subject to some concern at the time of production start-up. At the time GAZ was ordered to begin preparation for series production of the T-60, the required drawings for the 20mm TNSh installation were incomplete, mirroring the situation at KhTZ, thereby the GAZ plant was permitted until 15ᵗʰ August to install the 12.7mm DShK armament in the T-60 turret, with a further one month extension if necessary. Which considering GABTU formalized the contract with GAZ only on 21ˢᵗ August and that the plant was well behind schedule, indicates how the paper trails and manufacturing reality were often out of synch. As series production did not get underway until mid September GAZ was ultimately able to start T-60 production with the originally planned 20mm TNSh installed as main armament.

The production problems at GAZ were not only associated with delays in receiving hull and turret sets from sub-supplier plants. Some subcontractors, in a situation also reminiscent of the problems endured by KhTZ, never actually began to produce the parts desperately required by GAZ to complete their T-60 tanks. The "Dvigatel Revolutsii" (Engine of the Revolution) plant was for-instance expected to produce the final drives for the T-60 but by 18ᵗʰ September had produced not a single set, such that GAZ was forced to start manufacture of its own parts internal to the plant. The GAZ plant completed only 3 T-60 tanks in September 1941.

The start of T-60 production at GAZ naturally meant further demands on Model 202 engines (the tank version of the GAZ-11, also denoted as the GAZ-202) produced at GAZ. The plant had already proven unable to satisfy the demand for engines for the ill-fated production start-up at KhTZ in Kharkov, or supply the number of GAZ-11 engines required for the GAZ-61 wheeled vehicle series, which had recently entered production at GAZ.

As with the concurrent situation at KhTZ, the start-up of T-60 production at GAZ required direct ministry level intervention. At the beginning of September, the GAZ plant director I. K. Loskutov was summoned to a meeting of the Central Committee of the CPSU(b) - the Communist Party of the Soviet Union (TsK VKP(b)), chaired by G. M. Malenkov, where the GABTU leadership present demanded that all plant directors immediately increase efforts to maximize production. To have any chance of meeting the tank production requirements GAZ was forced to make difficult choices, and plant director Loskutov took the difficult decision to re-orientate GAZ production away from the assembly of light vehicles and trucks so as to concentrate on tank production, which would meet GABTU expectations, but in turn deprive the Red Army of also highly critical transport vehicles.

GABTU had concluded that GAZ should be capable of assembling 25 pre-series T-60 tanks in September; however this forecast proved optimistic, with GAZ completing precisely 3 tanks that month, largely due to supply difficulties with primary components such as hull and turret sets and engines, but also due to a lack of myriad other missing components. Hull and turret production was in particular exasperatingly slow. By 1st October, the Vyksunsky DRO, Murom and Novo-Kramatorsk plants had produced 6, 15 and 68 sets of hulls and turrets respectively, categorically ensuring GAZ could not achieve the GABTU production output targets for October. Full series production of the T-60 began at GAZ only in October 1941, late and behind schedule. The production target for the first five days of October was 15 tanks, against which GAZ completed precisely 5 tanks, though this increased exponentially to 69 tanks delivered by 20th October, with the primary reason for lower than expected T-60 production output remaining the unavailability of hull and turret sets from the three sub-supplier plants.

A GAZ production T-60 parked outside the assembly workshops, February 1942. (GAZ)

A side view of the same GAZ production tank, February 1942. (GAZ)

Many changes were introduced at GAZ to maximize production output. Within the first month of series production, the original rubber rimmed forged and welded road wheels were replaced with cast spoked metal types, reducing the use of rubber, which was in critically short supply. The production of command tanks was abandoned due to a consistent lack of radio sets, with the 80 sets of 71-TK-3 radios located at GAZ being released for use by other plants.

On 16th October 1941, the assembly of T-30 tanks was abandoned at Plant №37 (Moscow) as the plant underwent evacuation to Sverdlovsk. Within a matter of days afterwards, the KhTZ plant (Kharkov) was lost to the advancing German and Axis forces, such that from October 1941 GAZ in Gorky, located 400km to the east of Moscow, became the only remaining manufacturer of "small" (light) tanks in the Soviet Union. With its involuntary status as the sole producer of small tanks, the inability of GAZ to deliver in accordance with production requirements was clearly unacceptable. With Plant №37 safely on rails en-route to Siberia, Astrov and Okunev were dispatched to GAZ during the second week of October to ensure the required production output at GAZ was achieved. At their new Gorky location, Astrov became GAZ deputy chief designer and Okunev the senior military representative at the plant.

On 20th October a telegram arrived at GAZ signed by Stalin personally, demanding that T-60 production be increased to 10 tanks per day, approximately 10% more than the original October production plan agreed between GABTU and GAZ, with the well-travelled Malyshev being sent to GAZ (doubtless

also at Stalin's bequest) to ensure plant management were paying suitable attention.

Despite the obvious component supply problems, GAZ was able to slightly exceed its October production targets, completing 215 T-60 tanks in October 1941 as production ramped-up; however this production increase came at a high price; by the end of October wheeled vehicle production at GAZ was almost at a standstill. The GAZ-61-73 and its GAZ-61-416 wheeled artillery tractor variant were removed from production as they used the same basic GAZ-11 engine as mounted in the T-60; the GAZ-64 was also removed from production and the output of GAZ-AA and GAZ-AAA trucks was reduced to a trickle. Some machine tooling at GAZ was also now allocated to the production of PPSh sub-machine guns, mortars and "Katyusha" rockets, which all took a toll on wheeled vehicle production.

The GAZ plant built one of the more distinctive early variants of the T-60. At the time Plant №37 ceased production of the T-30 as it prepared to evacuate to Sverdlovsk, there remained nine completed T-30 tanks at the plant requiring rework before delivery, together with a quantity of T-30 hulls and conical turrets, all of which were marked for evacuation to GAZ with the trains transporting the plant tooling. The exact number of T-30 hull and turret sets actually sent to GAZ is unknown, but in the summer of 1942 GAZ still retained 47 T-30 sets in inventory. GAZ did not use the T-30 hulls in the assembly of complete tanks, but from October 1941 mounted the conical T-30 turrets on T-60 tanks, with a few of the "hybrid"

An up-armoured or "Ehkranirovanniy" GAZ production T-60, spring 1942. Note the additional turret and gun mantlet armour. (IZ)

tanks being displayed on Red Square on 7th November 1941. T-60 tanks mounting conical T-30 turrets produced at Plant Nº37 were used by the 33rd Separate Tank Brigade and the 108th Tank Brigade. Cast road wheels manufactured at Plant Nº37 were also used on early production tanks produced at GAZ.

GAZ managed to exceed the production plan target for November, with 471 tanks completed, despite the effects of Resolution Nº889ss issued on 11th November, which required GAZ to additionally deliver turretless T-60 tank chassis to Plant Nº113 "ZFS" (also located in Gorky) for installation of the 82mm M-8-24 "Katyusha" multiple rocket launcher system (MRS).

GAZ quickly recovered from its initial production start-up problems, managing to deliver 1314 (1323 per other sources) T-60 tanks for the full year 1941, in less than four months of series production. 1245 of these tanks were delivered to the Red Army (including a small quantity of turret-less chassis delivered to Plant Nº113 for mounting the M-8-24 MRS), the balance being sent to training schools. In under four months the GAZ plant in Gorky had changed from being a wheeled vehicle manufacturer with no experience of armoured vehicles of any description to become a major tank production plant, not only in Soviet terms, but worldwide. The Astrov design bureau (KB) at GAZ was also now de-facto the leading Soviet developer of small and light tanks. Due to its evacuation to Sverdlovsk and the protracted re-establishment of production there, Plant

Side view of the same GAZ production tank. The additional "Ehkranirovanniy" armour on the turret and the "secondary" gun mantlet shield is evident in this view. (IZ)

№37, where the "060" had been designed, lost its former position, with future design and development of the "060" and variants on the chassis being undertaken at GAZ.

As the T-60 entered series production at GAZ, the plant KB began parallel work on simplifying the design to maximize tank output. On 11th November 1941, the plant and KB management met to review simplification of the tank. The resulting resolution *"To ensure uninterrupted production of model "060" tanks in wartime"* as approved by the senior military GABTU KA representative at the plant listed a myriad of permitted production simplifications, including permission to interchange design components with available alternatives as parts availability dictated. There followed a long list of substantial changes that could be introduced at the plant as appropriate (see Appendix 2). The meeting and its conclusions legitimized simplifications already introduced of necessity at GAZ in late October 1941, an example being that Plant №34 in Moscow had stopped shipment of honeycomb type radiators, which were replaced by much simplified GAZ designed tubular core radiators. Some parts such as headlights were unavailable so many T-60 tanks were delivered in October without them, automoti-

ve headlights being "procured" at the front. The plant KB even investigated the option of replacing the rubber road wheel rims with laminated wooden rims as an emergency contingency, but this was not enacted. These and myriad other emergency measures remained in effect for only a few months, with tanks again being for-instance fitted with a full set of optics and instrumentation as they were being completed in February 1942.

With the arrival of the first winter of the war, it became apparent that the T-60 would benefit from some improvement in floatation on snow-covered terrain. The GAZ KB accordingly investigated alternative running gear arrangements. Tracks were designed with an increased length and pitch, and removable track grousers. Design work was also conducted on replacing the standard suspension and running gear with a modified type consisting of 8 smaller diameter road wheels on each side, to more evenly distribute ground pressure. The GAZ KB also developed an alternative spring based suspension system in the event that the supply of torsion bars was interrupted, but this likewise was not required. Meantime, the main priority at GAZ remained production output.

Overhead view of the same tank. The exhaust configuration, with the thermal-wrapped (asbestos) exhaust tube running over the engine deck to the GAZ-M1 derived exhaust silencer on the rear plate, was a feature of tanks produced at GAZ in the spring of 1942. (IZ)

Chapter 3

Re-Armament and Modernization

In addition to simplifying the T-60 for wartime series production, work began, initially at the GAZ KB, on modernizing the tank, almost from the day it had entered production. Early combat feedback indicated that the armour was insufficient, the frontal 15-20mm glacis armour being vulnerable not only to German anti-tank guns at any range, but also from infantry anti-tank rifles at typical engagement distances. The issue was addressed by Resolution GKO №893 dated 13th November 1941, which in addition to demanding increased tank production output from GAZ, also obligated the plant to develop a modified hull and turret with thicker armour.

The armour situation was addressed at a meeting held at GAZ on 16th November, attended by GAZ plant and KB design bureau management, and the chief of BTU GABTU KA, military engineer 1st rank B. M. Korobkov. The conclusion was that the frontal armour should be increased to 35mm, the driver-mechanic's "rubka" (the raised sponson section mounting the vision visor) and side armour to 25mm, and the turret armour to 25mm. As was the way in the Soviet Union, a prototype T-60 with additional armour plates on the hull and turret (referred to in Russian as T-60 "ekranirovanny" (literally screened or shielded armour) had already been built, and tested from 9th to 11th November - the week before the meeting at which the decision was taken to increase the armour thickness on the T-60. The prototype tank (serial №37790) was fitted with additional 10mm armour plates welded on the glacis, driver-mechanic's "rubka", and the lower frontal side armour and turret perimeter. The additional armour increased the combat weight of the T-60 by 360kg to 6150 kg.

For trials purposes the up-armoured tank was driven from the GAZ plant in Gorky to Vyksa and Murom and back to Gorky, a total distance of 457km, during which the tank suffered no significant reduction in speed, maneuverability or range due to the increased combat weight. The load on the torsion bars and running gear remained within permissible limits as did fuel consumption and oil and water temperatures. The modified tank was recommended for series production.

In parallel with the screening of the T-60, the plant KB also developed a modernized version of the tank, with increased base armour and incorporating many simplifications already introduced into series production tanks at GAZ from the second half of November 1941. In addition to the increased armour, the project envisaged a redesigned turret, with the air vent relocated to the turret hatch, increasing armour integrity, and various simplifications such as the use of a cast drive wheel without a separate bolted on (and thereby replaceable) drive sprocket ring, and a rear idler without a rubber rim. The project was experimental, but some elements were in modified form subsequently implemented into series production at GAZ and other plants.

Order №31ss of the People's Commissariat of the Tank Industry (NKTP) issued on 18th November 1941 obligated all tank plants to introduce the new "ekranirovanny" or shielded version of the T-60 developed by the KB at GAZ with immediate effect. Only Plant №176 (the locomotive plant named after Dzerzhinsky in Murom) was however in a position to immediately start manufacture of the new up-armoured hull and turret sets. The first set was completed on 19th November 1941, but output remained painfully slow; only 12

Plant №92 project to modify T-60 with new turret and 45mm armament. (TsAMO)

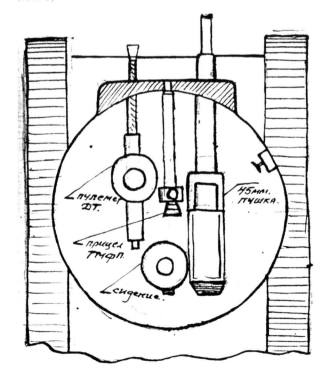

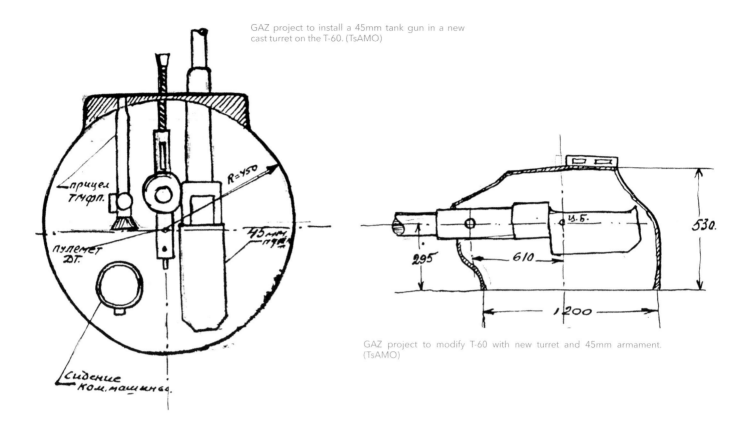

GAZ project to install a 45mm tank gun in a new cast turret on the T-60. (TsAMO)

GAZ project to modify T-60 with new turret and 45mm armament. (TsAMO)

sets were delivered in November and a further 35 in December, for a total production of 47 sets to the end of the year.

On 25th December 1941, Resolution GKO №1062ss "About the tanks T-34 and T-60" was issued, signed personally by Stalin. The resolution obligated NKTP, specifically Malyshev, to ensure the production of up-armoured "ekranirovanny" tanks as follows:

a) Produce from 15th January 1942, T-34 tanks with screened frontal armour of 60 mm, and from 15th February with (base) frontal armour of 60 mm;

b) Produce from 15th January 1942, T-60 tanks with screened frontal armour of 35 mm, and from 15th February with (base) frontal armour of 35 mm;

On 5th January Malyshev sent a letter to the NKTP production plants, reiterating Stalin's precise instructions. On 12th January 1942, a meeting was held with the participation of GAZ management and the chief of the 1st Department BTU GABTU KA, military engineer 1st rank I. D. Pavlov, at which the requirements for introducing screened T-60s were defined. The production documentation was subsequently sent to the armour production and T-60 assembly plants, namely Plant №37 (Sverdlovsk), Plant №38 (Kirov), Plant №176 (Murom), Plant №177 (Vyksa), Plant №178 (Kulebaki), Plant №180 (Saratov), Plant №264 (Krasnoarmeysk) and the "Red October" plant in Stalingrad). The armour thickness after screening was as shown in the table below, with part numbers assigned to the exhaustive list of armour plate in the original plant documents:

	Base armour (mm)	Additional screen armour (mm)
Hull glacis and frontal armour plates	20	15
Driver mechanic's "rubka" (front) plates	20	15
Driver mechanic's "rubka" (side) plates	20	10
Turret front, sides and rear plates	15	10

The lead in "ekranirovannie korpusov" (literally screened hulls but meaning hull and turret sets) was taken by Plant №176 in Murom, which had produced its first hull and turret set for GAZ by 19th November. According to a memorandum sent to GABTU on 10th January 1942, the plant had completed 26 hull and turret sets by 9th January, with full series production envisaged to start on 15th January. The plant completed 113 hull and turret sets in January, rising to 125 sets in February. The production of up-armoured hull and turret sets was meanwhile delayed at all other plants. Although it had increased the armour thickness of its base armour from 13mm to 15mm, Plant №177 in Vyksa had by 9th January not completed a single screened hull and turret set. Plant №178 meantime lacked the necessary production tooling. By 15th January the plant had a functioning steel guillotine for preparing parts, but a lack of piped oxygen for cutting and welding. It was also busy with other production including producing turrets and hull nose sections for the T-34, amoured cockpit plates for the LaGG-3 fighter aircraft and glacis armour plates for the NKL-26 aerosan. Due to the ongoing critical lack of oxygen, Plant №178 made the decision at a meeting held on 17th January 1942 to switch to the production of T-60 hull and turret sets made from thicker base armour rather than shielding lighter armoured sets, which

the plant nevertheless continued to do as circumstances allowed until the planned introduction of thicker base armour on 29th January. The first hull and turret set manufactured from thicker base armour was actually completed on 10th February. The plant's other priorities reduced output to 75 sets of T-60 armour in February and another 75 sets for the T-60 in March.

In the meantime, Plant №178 in December 1941 developed a conical cast turret for the T-60, similar to the welded type used on the T-30 and T-40, with an amour basis of 28-30mm, however the turret was not taken into series production. Similarly, the plant in April 1942 prepared a batch of cast driver-mechanic's observation hatches with an armour basis of 36-39 mm, but the prototypes suffered excessive armour cracking and the new hatches were also not taken into series production. The plant also developed and built a small quantity of cast roof hatches, with 15-20 fitted on production T-60 tanks.

Development work on hull and turret manufacture was also undertaken at other plants. From January 1942, hull and turret set production was organized at the MSTs-8 workshop within the GAZ plant. Armour plate was delivered to GAZ from Plant №112 (the "Krasnoe Sormovo" plant in the Sormovo district of Gorky, better know for T-34 tank production), and the Kuznetsky Metallurgical Plant (KMZ) located in Stalinsk.

The prototype GAZ-70 at the GAZ plant, February 1942. The GAZ-70 would later enter series production as the T-70, replacing the T-60. (GAZ)

The T-45 (T-60-2) prototype outside Plant №37 during prototype trials, late May 1942. (TsAMO)

GAZ completed only 50 hull and turret sets in January 1942, well short of its production target of 140 sets; due primarily to problems with both the availability and quality of steel delivered from Plant №112. KMZ began delivering armour plate to GAZ only in early February. In consequence, GAZ had by 18th February completed only 42 hull and turret sets, a fraction of its production target of 325 units.

Meantime, on 3rd January, GAZ had completed the first hull and turret set with 'ekranirovka" screened armour (albeit thereafter making only 7 sets for the month), and on 29th January the first hull and turret set with thicker base armour. Production at GAZ in February increased to 76 and 10 sets of each type respectively. The external appearance of T-60 tanks produced at GAZ and other plants reflected this parallel production of two different types of hull and turret set, which were in turn completed using a myriad of different sub-components, such that few T-60 tanks were identical in appearance as they left the production plant concerned.

The final plant involved in the production of the hull and turret sets for the GAZ assembled T-60 was Plant №180 (the Saratov rail wagon repair plant) in Saratov, to where the Izhorsk plant had been partially evacuated in late 1941. Plant №180 had originally been intended to produce T-50 hulls and turrets, but after the T-50 was removed from production the

plant was re-orientated towards T-60 production. After some start-up delays, Plant №180 began series production of T-60 hull and turret sets on 2nd February 1942, producing hull and turrets sets with thicker armour from the outset. The plant produced 50 hull and turrets sets in February against a target of 30, using sheet armour originally stockpiled for the T-50 with consequently slightly different armour thickness, the frontal armour being for-instance 37mm rather than 35mm in thickness. The downside of the better than expected production output was that 68% of the output suffered from cracks which required repair, with the same problems encountered with production from Plant №177.

By March 1942, five different plants were involved in hull and turret set production for GAZ, including the MSTs-8 workshop within the GAZ plant. By February, the quantity and quality of hull and turret set production had become acceptable, and the T-60 was finally being assembled with less of the supply difficulties that had plagued its early production. T-60 production had to be adjusted again in March 1942 however, but now for entirely new reasons related to changes in requirements at the front.

At the beginning of August 1941, during prototype testing of the TNSh tank variant of the 20mm ShVAK automatic cannon, the testing commission had noted that:

"the 20 mm ShVAK cannon mounted in the turret of the T-60 does not solve the problem of effectiveness against modern armoured vehicles with sloped armour with a thickness of 15-20mm. The Commission therefore considers it necessary to speed up work on developing more effective tank armament for the T-60".

In August 1941, when T-60 tank production was in its infancy, the 20mm ShVAK (TNSh) had been introduced as an alternative to the 12.7mm DShK which had been the main armament of the earlier T-40, and which had been considered entirely effective only a few months prior. However, under wartime conditions the need to rapidly upgrade armament was paramount and what was considered sufficient for the T-40 in 1940 was no longer valid for the T-60 in late 1941. The Artillery Committee of the Main Artillery Directorate of the Red Army (KA Artkom GAU) thereby in September 1941 initiated work on the installation of more powerful armament in the T-60. A meeting between the management of the GAZ KB and (artillery) Plant №92 in Gorky reviewed the available alternatives. The 20mm TNSh was not in of itself an ineffective weapon, and the first T-60s were delivered to the Red Army at the front only in October, a month after the meeting convened to review future armament options, so the matter was one of maintaining the T-60s effectiveness in a rapidly changing combat environment rather than being related directly to the weapon

itself. There were some later claims from front line Red Army units regarding the 20mm TNSh, but the majority of problems were related to improper operation of the weapon, and also the inconsistent quality of early ammunition deliveries.

Analysis of a number of captured German armoured vehicles in the first weeks of the war (the capturing and shipping eastward of which must in of itself be a fascinating story in the circumstances of the time) resulted in consideration being given to the standard T-60 turret being re-armed with the 45mm M-1938 tank gun which had been the standard armament of the T-26 and BT tanks and other armoured vehicles of the late 1930s. According to the initial plan, the new armament was to be developed as a collaborative effort between the GAZ KB and Plant №92, however the respective design bureaus ultimately developed two alternative options.

The Plant №92 alternative retained the original armament layout in the T-60 turret, with the 45mm M-1938 gun mounted on the right of the gun mantlet, the gun sight located in the centre and the DT machine gun mounted on the left. The commander's turret seat was centrally located between the gun and DT machine gun, as with the original T-60 design, but offset to the rear of the turret. The main armament was fired by a button located on the handle of the turret traverse mechanism; the DT machine gun was fired by means of a button on the handle of

The distinctive 45mm turret mantlet is evident in this frontal view of the T-45 (T-60-2). (TsAMO)

This overhead view of the T-45 (T-60-2) prototype clearly shows the modified turret, extended at the front to accommodate the 45mm armament and with a turret bustle as a counterweight at the rear. (TsAMO)

The T-45 (T-60-2) prototype with its 45mm armament begins to clearly resemble the later production T-70. (TsAMO)

The T-45 (T-60-2) prototype was built on an "old" hull, with riveted hull side amour, whereas the plant had at the time begun to weld the hulls on production tanks. The significantly modified turret is evident in this view. (TsAMO)

the elevation mechanism. With the drawings complete, Plant №92 awaited approval to manufacture a prototype in metal.

The GAZ KB alternative developed under the guidance of N.A. Astrov as chief designer was altogether more radical, with the weapon layout changed. The sight was relocated to the left, with the DT machine gun mounted in its original location, with the commander's position also moved further to the left side of the turret. This required the elevation and traverse mechanisms to be relocated and the turret ammunition racks to be reconfigured. Although the GAZ developed T-60 was a more radical modification, it gave the tank commander more working space. While the Plant №92 alternative had been developed with working drawings ready for approval, GAZ had meantime not only built a prototype but also subjected it to firing trials, such that the very existence of the GAZ prototype gave the variant a distinct advantage.

Both projects were submitted for consideration on 20th December 1941. Each project as proposed had its strengths and weaknesses; however the main problem was that the increased weight of the 45mm M-1932/38 tank gun made the turret unstable, particularly when rotating with the gun set at high elevation. A turret bustle with a 30kg counterweight was proposed to balance the turret; however the main problem remained that a 45mm gun installation in the minimalist T-60 turret made the commander-gunner's already tight position worse, and made operation of the turret rotation mechanisms difficult. The commander also continued his other role of gun-

ner/loader, which was not such an issue with the standard T-60 as the 20mm TNSh was an automatic gun with magazine feed; however manually reloading individual 45mm rounds in the tight T-60 turret greatly reduced the potential rate of fire.

On 20th December a memorandum tasked GAZ and Plant №92 to complete their 45mm re-armament projects on 15th and 20th January respectively, to test the weapons and provide a report on the conclusions, though the GAZ project at the time still remained the preferred option.

Concurrently with the installation of a 45mm M-1938 gun in the standard turret, GAZ was also permitted to manufacture a new and now cast turret with the turret ring diameter increased by 25-30mm, also to be subjected to firing trials on 15th January. Per Soviet reality norms, the cast turret and armament combination was already under development, under the design leadership of V.A. Dedkov, as the official permissions filtered through.

T-60-1 (ZiS-60) Prototype

The ZiS-60 (also known as the "061" or T-60-1) was developed at the ZiS automotive plant in the autumn of 1941 as a plant initiative in collaboration with Plant №37. The T-60-1 considered modification of an otherwise standard T-60 in order to accommodate a more power ZiS-16 petrol engine developing 88hp. The modifications, which were supervised by B.M. Fitterman at ZiS and were confined to enlargement and reconfiguration of the hull to accommodate the alternative and more powerful engine installation, were carried out on a standard T-60, with the prototype being completed in February 1942, fitted with a ZiS-60 engine now uprated to 95hp with a potential of increasing power output to 110hp. The ultimate aim of the project was to maintain the mechanical performance of the T-60 despite the increase in combat weight as a result of up-armouring of the hull and turret. The ZiS plant was evacuated from Moscow to Miass, and Plant №37 evacuated from Moscow to Sverdlovsk while the ZiS-60 was being developed, and although the Podolsk armour plant had apparently built ten hull and turret sets to the new ZiS-60 specification, by February 1942 when the prototype was completed, a potential replacement for the T-60 had already been developed and a prototype of that alternative tank already built at GAZ.

GAZ-70 1ˢᵗ Prototype

While considering alternative armament options to prolong the service life of the T-60 series as long as practical, the GAZ plant KB headed by Astrov in December 1941 also began development of a much more radical design change for the T-60, with V.A. Dedkov taking the lead design role on the new prototype. The "ekranirovka", or shielding, of the base tank armour, together with the proposed increase in armament calibre, significantly increased the T-60s combat weight, which in turn

had an effect on overall mobility. While modifying the T-60 turret and armament was an interim solution, the entire tank would need to be redesigned to accept higher levels of armament and armour, and hence additional combat weight.

By 14ᵗʰ February 1942 a prototype of the new radical development of the T-60 had been completed, which received plant index GAZ-70*. The new design featured a lengthened hull with an additional road wheel station and return roller on each side, a new turret cast with a wider turret ring diameter, and a 45mm M-1932/38 (20K) tank gun as main armament. The armour was increased to 45 mm on the glacis (matching early that of production T-34s), which inevitably increased the combat weight to approximately 7.5-8.0 metric tonnes. In order to compensate for the weight increase and maintain overall performance and maneuverability the new tank was now powered by a twin GAZ-202 engine installation (the dual engine installation being designated GAZ-203). Having in effect developed an entirely new tank type, which would later enter series production as the T-70, GAZ had leapfrogged its own proposed 45mm armament upgrade of the standard T-60 tank, which was consequently abandoned.

T-60 with 37mm ZiS-19 Tank Gun - 1ˢᵗ Prototype

The T-60 modified with the 45mm M-1938 (20K) tank gun, as

T-60 with prototype 37mm ZiS-19 installation during trials, February 1942. (TsAMO)

*The GAZ-70 is sometimes referred to as the "070"; however the "010" series of project numbers was internal to Plant №37, while the prototype for what would become the T-70 was designed at GAZ and thereby given the traditional GAZ index, hence GAZ-70, and when accepted for production, T-70.

The same vehicle as on p. 37, with its gun at maximum elevation. (TsAMO)

developed by Plant №92, also failed to progress beyond initial trials stage. The primary reason for this was that Plant №92 had since August 1941 been developing a new 37-mm tank gun as a plant initiative under the direction of V.G. Grabin, based on the ballistics of the 37-mm M-1939 (61-K, ZiK-37) automatic anti-aircraft gun, and using the same ammunition. The new tank gun was both lighter and simpler to manufacture, having an overall weight of 235 kg including mounting (reduced from 403kg for the M-1932/38) and consisting of 153 parts (versus 436 parts for the 45-mm tank gun M-1932/38). ArtKom GAU made the following "recommendation" to GAZ plant management with regard to the new weapon:

"As the 45 mm gun has large dimensions for installation in the existing T-60 turret, for the future, you should consider a new 37 mm tank gun designed by Plant №92 (General-Major Grabin). Prototypes of this gun will be ready by 15th January 1942. You should request Plant №92 to accelerate preparation of a prototype of the 37 mm tank gun, for installation in a T-60 by 1st February 1942."

The Plant №92 project to install a 45mm M-1938 tank gun in the standard T-60 turret was meantime not officially dropped, however work moved on to a new 37mm tank gun alternative, with Plant №92 concentrating development on its in-house 37mm design. The working drawings were

completed by 13th January 1942, the weapon receiving the plant index ZiS-19. The prototype was completed at Plant №92 on 19th January and immediately shipped to GAZ for installation in a modified T-60 turret. In parallel, the drawings and specifications for the new gun were meantime sent to GAZ on 14th January, the day after they were completed, so the latter plant could modify a T-60 turret for installation of the new weapon. On 19th January, the same day it was completed at Plant №92, the gun was delivered to GAZ, from where Plant №92 received their prototype 37mm ZiS-19 back on 27th January, now mounted in a modified T-60 turret.

Installation of the 37mm ZiS-19 gun in a series production T-60 turret required only minimal changes to the turret design, particularly when compared with the modifications required for installing the 45mm M-1932/38 tank gun as also developed by Plant №92 in cooperation with GAZ. The commander's seat was moved slightly to the left, similar to the GAZ design, and the gun cradle and mask modified. The TMFP sight was retained, as was the 7.62mm DT co-axial machine gun, with a new design of welded gun mantlet bolted to the gun mask. Firing was by means of a push-button trigger. Due to the compact recoil mechanism being located above the gun barrel, the 37mm ZiS-19 gun was not significantly bulkier than the 20mm TNSh.

The 37mm ZiS-19 tank gun was marginally more compact than the 45mm alternative, and used less parts in manufacture. The main issue related to available proven ammunition for the weapon. (TsAMO)

37mm ZiS-19 during hydraulic test trials. (TsAMO)

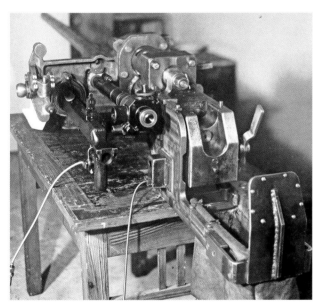

The fabricated 37mm ZiS-19 gun mantlet developed for the T-60. (TsAMO)

For trials purposes the ZiS-19 mounted in its modified turret was installed on a T-60 that had been delivered by GAZ on 10th December 1941,with test firing undertaken from 21st to 24th February 1942, with 181 test rounds fired. The tests were satisfactory; however it was acknowledged that the systems was uncomfortable for the commander-gunner to operate, as he could not stand up straight within the tank to operate the weapon. An alternative reclining saddle-seat was suggested for the commander's awkward turret seat, while in a rare moment of ergonomic concern it was also suggested to mount protective smooth metal panels round the turret race to prevent the commander-gunner from impaling himself on sharp edges. The tests concluded that:

"1. Production of the ZiS-19 by comparison with the 45-mm tank gun is much cheaper, and requires less machine tooling and labour; also the 37 mm tank gun has several times less parts and is therefore simpler to manufacture. Altogether, this can significantly increase the mass production of tank guns.

2. The armour penetration is practically identical to that of the 45 mm tank gun; but the ZiS-19 allows for a greater ammunition complement due to the lesser dimensions and weight of 37 mm rounds.

3. The 37 mm ZiS-19 tank gun can be presented for state trials."

Competitive state trials between the Plant №92 T-60 armed with the 37mm ZiS-19, and the GAZ T-60 with its reconfigured

The first prototype of the 37mm ZiS-19 armed T-60 with the main armament at maximum and minimum elevation. (TsAMO)

turret mounting the 45 mm M-1938 tank gun were authorized by Artkom GAU KA on 27th February 1942, to be conducted at the ANIOP polygon (Gorokhovets) from 9th March 1942. What transpired was somewhat different.

GAZ-70 (T-70) - Modified Prototype

On 19th February 1942, two days before the firing tests of the ZiS-19 mounted in its GAZ supplied T-60, the GAZ plant had meantime begun tests of a further modification developed at GAZ on the basis of the GAZ-70 prototype, which was effectively an ongoing modification of the original GAZ-70 project. The new design, which latterly received the official designation T-70, had increased armour and a corresponding combat weight of 9.0 metric tonnes. The tank was fitted with a cast turret manufactured by Plant №178, with the maximum armour thickness increased from 28-30mm to 50mm, which would be replaced on production T-70 tanks with a simplified welded design. The turret ring was increased to 1200mm, and the working conditions of the commander (who remained also gunner/loader) significantly enhanced. Testing of the T-70 was completed on 24th February, with the following conclusions:

"1. The combat and tactical capabilities of the T-70 are much superior to those of the T-60, assemblies and parts of which are also used in the design of the T-70.

2. All the main indicators of characteristics of the T-70, armament, armour, medium speed, maneuverability, traction in snow and visibility exceed the corresponding indices of the T-60, giving the opportunity to use the T-70 as a light tank, able to engage with small calibre anti-tank guns, light and small tanks, infantry and mechanized enemy troops, and also to serve as tanks in direct support of infantry.

3. The T-70 light tank can be adopted for the Red Army and put into series production to replace the T-60.

The remaining paragraphs required the correction of deficiencies and for GAZ to continue testing the components of the T-70 in the spring and summer in parallel with the launch of series production of the new tank type.

The limited development potential of the T-60 on its existing chassis had been well understood at GAZ, and the plant KB had thereby chosen to develop a new tank, which entirely met GABTU requirements. The timing of the new tank development was also not incidental. The T-50 had been removed from production according to Resolution GKO №1114 dated 6th January 1942 due to increasing difficulty with re-establishing production at Plant №174 after the plant's evacuation from its original location, with the plant ultimately converting to the production of KV parts. The

T-70 was not a direct replacement for the technically more complex T-50, but had identical armament and was suitable for production in plants with simpler production tooling and assembly capability. As the 37mm ZiS-19 and 45mm M-1938 armed T-60 variants were being prepared for state trials, the T-60's ultimate replacement had already successfully completed plant trials within the same GAZ plant. GAZ thereby sent its "modified" tank design for the allotted state trials on 18th April, but the tank now sent to the ANIOP polygon was not a T-60 re-armed with a 45mm M-1938 tank gun as originally envisaged, but the prototype for the T-70.

On 6th March 1942 Decree №1395 was issued *"about organization of production of T-70 tanks at the Gorky Molotov Automobile Plant, NKSM."* in accordance with which the T-60 was to be replaced in production by the T-70 at GAZ from March 1942.

T-60 production at GAZ was gradually wound down as the T-70 began to be assembled as its replacement, though the start-up problems with the T-70 at GAZ replicated those earlier encountered with the T-60, with high scrap rates on cast components and a shortage of the required grade of steel for the torsion bars retarding production. The T-70 production target at GAZ for March 1942 was 20 tanks, however only 3 were completed, and those without turrets, such that the start-up of series production was rescheduled for 14th April.

Despite the fact that since 6th March the T-60 was being phased out of production to be replaced by the T-70, the T-60 continued to be produced in quantity, and also to be modified. Somewhat ironically, it was only from February 1942 that the T-60 began to be built to its original design specification, incorporating many original design components for which substitutes had of necessity been found in the preceding months. Final production T-60s were fitted with forged and welded road wheels and a new exhaust system including the silencer taken from the new T-70. GAZ produced 320 T-60s in March (20 without turrets), and a further 138 in April (14 without turrets), after which T-60 production at GAZ was finally terminated. The run-out of T-60 production was not thereby an instant process. As of 1st April 1942 the plant had 608 T-60 hulls in inventory, of which 379 were assembled from 20mm base armour, 97 with added "ekranirovannikh" armour, and 132 with increased base armour. Allowing for the 138 T-60s produced in April, there remained a large number of assembled T-60 hulls at GAZ, for which the plant would later find a novel use.

When T-60 production ceased in April 1942, the T-60 had been in production at GAZ for a period of only 8 months, during which it had delivered 2913 T-60 tanks to the Red Army. As of 1st July 1942, GAZ still retained 13 completed

T-60s with serious manufacturing defects, which were rebuilt at the plant, with the last 5 T-60 tanks produced being sent to the 1st Gorky Tank School on 15th August 1942.

T-60 with 37mm ZiS-19 - 2nd Prototype

Despite GKO Resolution №1395 terminating T-60 production in favour of the T-70, Plant №92 nevertheless completed its experimental installation of the 37mm ZiS-19 in the T-60. The weapon was now installed in a radically redesigned wedge-shaped turret form that had little resemblance to the standard T-60 turret, of which only the lower section remained unaltered. The new turret significantly improved the working position for the multi-tasking commander/gunner/loader. The turret hatch was moved to the rear plate, with a viewing device from the T-70 now installed in the roof. The 37mm armament was mounted in a mantlet similar in form to that used on the T-70. The gun sight was moved to the left, and in its place was installed a DT machine-gun. The result was a turret with better internal space and improved combat capability. Testing of the modified T-60 with its 37mm ZiS-19 armament

commenced at the Gorokhovets polygon on 19th April, as the new GAZ T-70 was in transit to the polygon for competitive trials. Testing showed that the weapon had good armour penetration, rate of fire and accuracy; however the 37mm ZiS-19 with its high muzzle velocity was predicted to have a significantly shorter barrel life than the 45mm M-1938, while the 37mm "OF" (high explosive) ammunition was much less effective than 45mm "OF" ammunition. The latter was a significant defect considering that a main task of Red Army small and light tanks was infantry support and the suppression of enemy infantry. New ammunition could be procured without difficulty. As an alternative to the 45mm M-1938, the 37mm ZiS-19 gun was however simpler to manufacture and half the weight, so with a few defects remedied the gun was nevertheless accepted for installation in the new T-70, as a replacement for the 45mm tank gun that had been in service in various modifications since the early 1930s.

The original concept of re-arming the T-60 with the ZiS-19, the reason that the prototype had been developed, had however been overtaken by events. By the time the prototype

The second prototype T-60 fitted with the 37mm ZiS-19 armament in a new and enlarged turret. Plant trials, summer 1942 (TsAMO)

Front and rear view of the second T-60 37mm ZiS-19 armed prototype with new turret. (TsAMO)

Interior views of the T-60 with ZiS-19, summer 1942 (TsAMO)

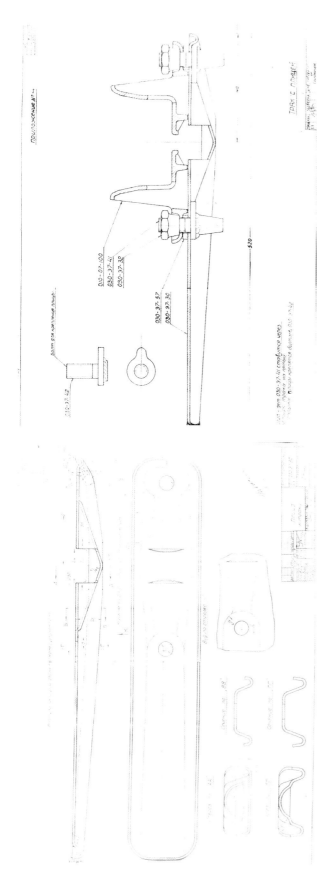

was completed the T-60 had effectively been made redundant by the arrival of T-70, and this was confirmed in a Resolution issued at the beginning of July 1942, which removed the T-60 from production at Plant №37, Plant №38 and Plant №264. The 37mm ZiS-19 tank gun as a consideration for armament on the T-70 was however also overtaken by events, as work was already advanced on a new 45mm tank gun with a lengthened barrel, the 45mm VT-42.

In addition to the theme of re-arming the T-60 with 37mm or 45mm alternative armament, the potential of re-arming the T-60 with the 23mm VYa-23 aircraft cannon developed at TsKB-14 also resurfaced in a significantly modified form in the summer of 1942. A letter signed by Volkov and Yartsev sent to the leadership of GABTU KA on 28th July 28, 1942 stated:

"At present, in order to improve the armour penetration of German tanks and armoured vehicles, at the request of the command of the VVS KA (the Red Army Air Force) we have developed a gun "VYa" chambered for 23mm but with a 14.5mm round, the armour-piercing capability of which should be up to 90mm (due to higher muzzle velocity of the round). The 23mm calibre "VYa" cannon is in service with the VVS KA and is currently produced in NKV plants. Transitioning the 23mm "VYa" to 14.5mm calibre requires changing only the barrel and receiver, which changes can be easily introduced into expanded production. Based on the foregoing, we deem the "VYa" gun with 14.5mm calibre (rounds) for use in tanks. According to our assumptions, the 14.5mm calibre "VYa" gun can be installed in a light tank. We request your permission to install a prototype 14.5mm calibre "VYa" gun into a tank at one of the plants of the tank industry."

This initiative was also not implemented, as at the time of the above request to install a prototype 14.5mm version of the "VYa" into the T-60, the tank was already being removed from production and alternative armament options thereby deemed irrelevant.

Drawings of the track extensions developed for the T-60 at Plant №37, January 1942. (RGAZ)

Chapter 4

T-60 Production at Plant №264 (Krasnoarmeisk), №37 (Sverdlovsk), №38 (Kirov)

As the old saying goes, no battle plan survives first combat engagement, and this was the case with the T-60. The T-60 had been designed at Plant №37 for production at Plant №37 (Moscow), KhTZ (Kharkov) and GAZ (Gorky), but within a matter of weeks thereafter, KhTZ had been lost to advancing Wehrmacht and Axis forces, and Plant №37 was being evacuated on rails to Sverdlovsk, leaving GAZ for a time as the only plant assembling T-60 tanks. It would be the combined production capability of GAZ, Plant №264 (Krasnoarmeisk), Plant №38 (Kirov) and the relocated Plant №37 (Sverdlovsk) that would determine T-60 tank production, aided by a complex network of hull and turret set and component suppliers the majority of which had also been relocated and re-established far to the east of their original locations. Neither the plants nor the locations that would see T-60 production through until replacement by the T-70 were those envisaged when the T-60 was being designed on the drawing boards at Plant №37 in the summer of 1941.

T-60 Production at Plant №264 (Krasnoarmeisk)

In 1931, the Krasnoarmeisk shipyard was founded in the village of Krasnoarmeisk (also known as Sarepta), at that time a suburb of Stalingrad, for the production of small river vessels. The shipyard was renamed Plant №264 of the People's Commissariat of the Shipbuilding Industry (NKSP) in 1940, and henceforth also began production of Project 1124 armoured river launches, originally armed with T-28 turrets and later (from 1942) with T-34 turrets. The same year, Plant №264 began production of T-34 hull and turret sets for the nearby Stalingrad Tractor Plant (STZ), such that by June 1941 the plant was well experienced in the production of armour.

With the outbreak of war in June 1941, Plant №264 was instructed to concentrate purely on the production of armoured vehicles. In mid August the engineers Krasilshikov and Nemchinsky wrote a letter to Stalin and the Commissar of Shipbuilding (NKSP) I. I. Nosenko, with a proposal to build armoured tractors at Plant №264 on the basis of the STZ-5 artillery tractor. The letter was forwarded to GABTU, from whence the head of the GABTU KA Lieutenant-General Ya. Fedorenko personally responded that:

"I think that we need to focus all attention not on armoured tractors and armoured trucks, but on the mass production of T-50 and T-60 light tanks."

Fedorenko's reply was direct, but also highly prophetic. The Kharkov Tractor Plant (KhTZ) was at the time being prepared for evacuation, as was the Mariupol Plant, which had produced hull and turret sets for T-34 tanks built at KhTZ in Kharkov. In mid September the first machine tooling and parts from KhTZ arrived in Stalingrad, where they were delivered to Plant №264, which continued to produce Project 1124 armoured launches, but was increasingly orientated on tank production. The KhTZ design bureau decamped to Plant №264 together with the machine tooling and on 11th September 1941 the plant was transferred from the Commissariat of the Shipbuilding Industry (NKSP) to the people's Commissariat of Tank Industry (NKTP). A curiosity of the increase in tank production at Plant №264 and its inherited tooling, drawings and personnel is that the plant technical documentation was stamped "KhTZ" rather than Plant №264 until the end of 1941.

The production of T-60 tanks at Plant №264 was very much inter-related with T-34 production at the STZ plant along the river. With the outbreak of war, in accordance with a Resolution of the SNK SSSR i TsK VKP (b) the T-34 production target at STZ for the second half of 1941 was increased from 1000 to 1405 tanks, the latter figure being increased further to 1585 tanks after the evacuation of Plant №183 from Kharkov. Plant №264 was tasked with building hull and turret sets for the T-34, but had limited casting facilities compared with Mariupol. From September 1941, a simplified hull was developed for series production at Plant №264, for which the armoured steel plate was tempered and rolled as at other plants, but built to a distinctive design developed by engineers at STZ and Plant №264 in combination with the NII-48 institute, whereby the plates were now interlocked with chamfering required only where they were aligned with the hull roof and hull floor. This, together with deletion of the first and high temperature tempering processes reduced T-34 hull assembly time from 200 to only 36 hours, and thereby greatly increased output as delivered to STZ for final assembly. The hull design was again modified from September as a result of combat feedback.

Concurrent with T-34 hull production, Plant №264 had from September also started to produce turrets for the T-34, which were constructed of welded rolled plate armour and using the same simplified tempering process as adopted for the hulls, as Plant №264 did not have sufficient foundry facilities to produce the volume of T-34 turrets required by STZ. Plant №264 would attempt to produce cast turrets for the T-34 from February 1942, but due to lack of resources full series production began only in July 1942.

Plant №264 was from the autumn of 1941 clearly preoccupied with the production of T-34 hull and turret sets for delivery to the STZ plant in Stalingrad for final assembly, exactly at the time when it was also tasked with starting the production of complete T-60 tanks in addition to hull and turret sets for the T-34.

Plant №264 clearly had recent experience of producing armoured hull and turret sets for the T-34, but in the autumn of 1941 this was an all-consuming task, and preparing for assembly of less powerful T-60 small tanks was understandably not viewed as a priority at the plant. With other tank and tank component plants similarly overloaded with work, Plant №264 was forced to develop T-60 production practically from scratch, which it nevertheless accomplished in the period October - November 1941, with production starting in incomplete and unheated assembly and machine shop buildings. As Plant №264 was more than busy with the urgent production of T-34 hull and turret sets for the nearby STZ plant it accordingly concentrated on the final assembly of T-60s, becoming the only T-60 production plant which did not build its own hull and turret sets, the plant receiving the majority of its hull and turrets sets from the "Red October" plant in Stalingrad. Other parts including road wheels, radiators and fuel tanks were provided by STZ to which Plant №264 delivered T-34 hull and turret sets, with parts for T-60 production at Plant №264

doubtless being the return loads. The first T-60 was completed at Plant №264 on 29th September 1941, with the transmission and running gear provided from Plant №76 (STZ).

On 9th November 1941, GKO Resolution №876ss was issued "On the re-establishment of tank plants evacuated from Kharkov, Moscow and Leningrad". According to the resolution, the installation of production tooling equipment at Plant №264 was to be completed by 1st December, with delivery of the first 30 T-60 tanks in November and 150 in December. By 15th January 1942 planned production was expected to be 10 tanks daily, or over 300 for the month. The reality was somewhat different. Despite significant teething problems, the plant had almost completed the installation of production tooling by the end of November, but due to a lack of engines had not completed a single tank, the first three engines arriving at the plant only on 29th November. The production target for December was increased to 200 tanks to compensate, but in fact only 45 tanks were completed that month, now due to a lack of hull and turret sets, of which Plant №264 had only 37 sets available as production commenced, together with 13 hulls produced by the "October Revolution" plant in Voroshilovgrad, built with 20mm armour plate and fitted with screened armour locally at Plant №264. The "October Revolution" plant was to have produced another 100 hull and turrets sets in December, but managed only 7 sets. The problems were compounded by a lack of parts from STZ, which in December delivered only 39 radiators and 91 fuel tanks, with severe delays on track and other components. Despite all the problems, Plant №264 completed its first 5 T-60 tanks on 8th December, and would quickly become second only to GAZ in the production of T-60 tanks urgently required by the Red Army. The start-up problems with unavailable components did not quickly recede however, the situation in January 1942 being reported by Military Representative 2nd Rank Morozov:

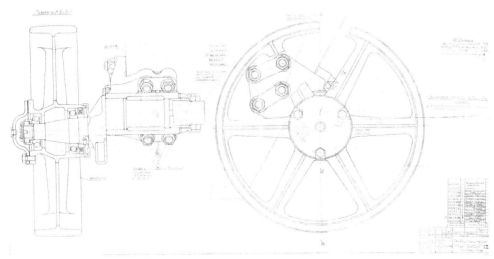

Plant drawing of the rear idler without rubber rim, developed at the KB of Plant №38 in the winter of 1941 and used in production at the plant from April 1942.

"On the instructions of the People's Commissariat, Plant №264 was to produce 240 T-60 tanks in the month of January. In fact it produced 101 tanks and shipped 94, with 17 tanks in the process of completion. The main reasons for the failure of the program were the following:

1) Poor supply of hulls from the Red October plant (military representative Comrade Mezhbizher). The January production plan was for 200 hulls, in fact 92 were delivered, these incomplete, with a number of deficiencies that had to be remedied by Plant №264.

2) Failure of supply from the STZ plant. For example, for the month of January 450 radiators and fuel tank sets should have been delivered, in fact it delivered 102 radiators, and fuel tanks for 100 tanks.

As regards cold forged, forged, iron and steel cast parts, STZ has also failed in its task to provide these parts, due to mechanical and assembly workshop downtime. Regarding cold forging deliveries from the STZ plant, the question was raised at the meeting of the City Committee of the CPSU(b), the written findings of which record that STZ, due to its poor performance in supplying parts, was disrupting the production of tanks at Plant №264.

The third reason for the failure of the January production plan is down to failures at plant №264, which result from the manufacturing of mass quantities of (new) parts and the assembly of tanks. Currently, the start-up period is complete, the main production tooling installed and if there is sufficient supply of parts the mechanical shop can give deliver 10 hull and turret sets per day, and the assembly shop on receiving required parts can deliver 6-7 tanks per day, and in 15-20 days can bring the assembly up to 10 tanks daily.

The report went on to detail the situation at the plant as it worked on the February production target. There were only 8 hulls in the plant, 3 radiators, and no fuel tanks whatsoever. There were 18 engines available, but nearly all had defects requiring rework. There were no belt links or rounds for the 20mm TNSh armament, no gun sights and no F-1 grenades. There were no signal horns, and brake bands only for 20 tanks, the suggested solution for the latter being to replace the lined "Ferrodo" brake bands with cast iron alternatives, though it was admitted that tests on the latter were not complete. The report concluded with a statement that there was a lack of qualified technicians for performing GABTU KA acceptance tests, and that such higher skillsets were limited within the plant and new technicians difficult to recruit, the latter issue being reported (somewhat bizarrely considering the circumstances) as being down to low pay. Despite T-60 production always being secondary to hull and turret production for T-34 assembly at STZ, Plant №264 still managed to assemble and deliver 52 T-60 tanks in December 1941.

The problem of lack of parts supply from STZ was so acute that tanks were delivered without some key components. At least 11 tanks were delivered in January without oil coolers. Tanks were over-painted with white nitrose based paint rather than the water based chalk and lime whitewash used for centuries, which though a technicality also indicates that the tanks were painted for winter as they left the plant rather than it always being done by the Red Army in the field. Meantime, Plant №180 (the Podolsk armour plant), which was evacuated from the Moscow suburbs to the premises of Plant №178 (the

Plant drawing of the track guards and ZIP (spare parts) storage, as developed by the KB at KhTZ in August 1941 and built at Plant №264 from the spring of 1942. (TsAMO)

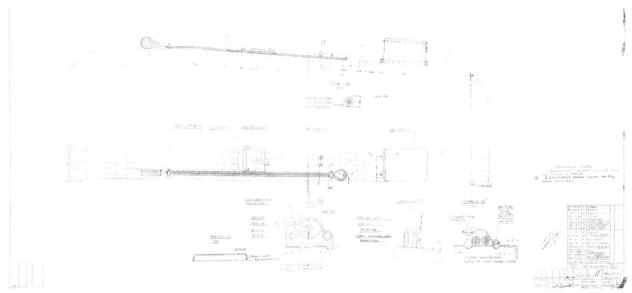

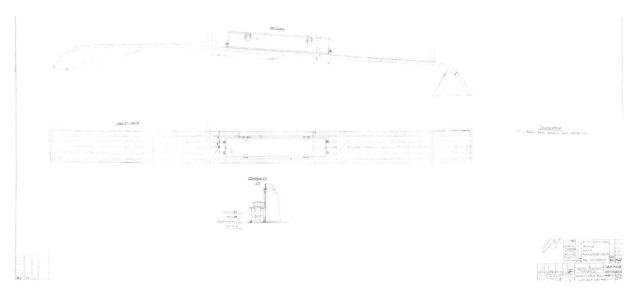

Plant drawing of the track guards and ZIP (spare parts) storage box, as developed by the KB at Plant №264 in January 1942 and built at the plant from the spring of 1942. (TsAMO)

Kulebaki armour plant near Saratov) began assembly of hull and turret sets for Plant №264. Plant №177 (with production facilities evacuated from the Vyksa DRO "Vyksunsky" plant to Murom) also began limited scale production of T-60 hull and turret sets. These additional production assets greatly improved the earlier production supply chain situation.

Despite all of the problems at Plant №264 and STZ, GABTU considered the situation as inevitable and temporary, and on 30th January 1942 an agreement was signed between Plant №264 and GABTU for the supply of 650 tanks, at a cost of 81,000 rubles for a fully equipped line tank and 82,700 rubles for commander's tanks fitted with radio. Meantime in December 1941, feedback from the Battle for Moscow and other combat operations had indicated the increasing use of 50mm and 75mm anti-tank weapons by German and Axis forces, as a result of which GKO Resolution №1062 had been issued requiring the frontal armour on the T-34 to be increased to 60mm. On 28th December 1941 a group of NII-48 engineers at Plant №264 under the leadership of Kofman began developing "ekranirovka" or screening for the T-34 using the same armour plate used for screening the T-60s produced at Plant №264. As production began to stabilize at Plant №264, the output for January 1942 was at 102 tanks almost double that achieved in December 1941.

Other plants were brought into the Plant №264 supply chain to produce parts that had proven problematical to source. Plant №469 NKAP in Gorky, which had produced radiators for Plant №37 and GAZ, was for-instance in mid-February instructed to increase overall production to supply all plants producing the T-60.

Meantime, only weeks after the 30th January GABTU de-

cision to contract for the delivery of 650 T-60 tanks with Plant №264, the GAZ plant began to move away from T-60 production as the plant geared up for assembly of the T-70 light tank, which began in March 1942. The decision was taken however to continue T-60 hull and turret production at GAZ and deliver these excess sets to Plant №264 for final T-60 assembly.

Plant №264 had been expected to produce 200 T-60 tanks in February 1942, but only 67 were delivered. This was again down to many factors, not least a lack of available hull and tur-

Plant drawing of the all-cast roadwheel with internal amortization developed at the KB of Plant №264 in December 1941, and produced at the plant from April 1942. (TsAMO)

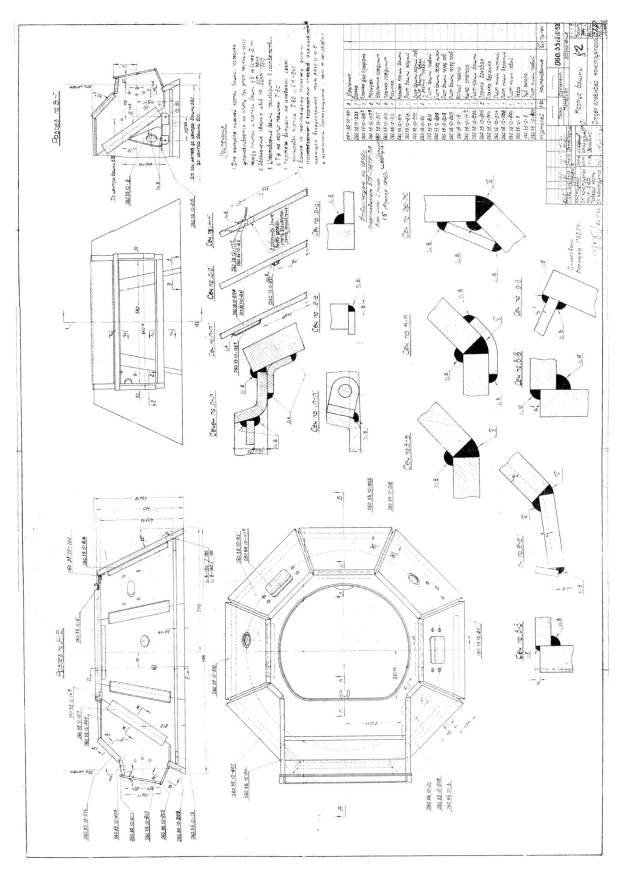

Plant drawing of an experimental modernization of the original T-60 turret developed at the KB of Plant №264 in February 1942.

ret sets. The Red October plant was to have supplied 250 hull and turret sets but delivered only 159 in February, of which only 61 sets were delivered in the first half of the month. Plant №180 meantime failed to deliver a single hull and turret set to Plant №264.

Engine supply was also critical, with the number of T-60 tanks produced at Plant №264 in February 1942 being equal to the number of engines available for installation. The list of deficient deliveries was long - 90 radiators delivered against a requirement for 300, 183 fuel tanks in lieu of 600, 165 brake bands in lieu of 1200 required, and 256 road wheels (enough for 32 tanks, or 25 if also used as idlers) against a requirement for 2000, and those delivered still required to be sent out to have rubber rims added. The production problems were clearly immense but not confined to T-60 production. T-34 tanks delivered by STZ were until September 1941 built with V-2 diesel engines delivered from Plant №75 in Kharkov before its evacuation. STZ had from October 1941 started building its own V-2 diesel engines but with problems in quality, quanti-

ty and reduced power output, and due to lack of alternatives had also installed V-2V engines from the "Voroshilovets" artillery tractor, and from October 1941 had also begun to install M-17T tank and M-17F aviation engines approved at a GKO meeting on 4th October 1941 as a legitimate alternative engine installation for the T-34 and the KV in desperate circumstances. STZ between October 1941 and April 1942 delivered 562 T-34 tanks fitted with M-17 series petrol engines, which gives some perspective as to the difficulty Plant №264 was experiencing in sourcing components for a strategically less crucial tank like the T-60 which was also competing for parts availability. Stalin would later in 1942 praise the directors and management of Plant №112, the director of STZ (Dulkin) and the director of Plant №264 (Shcherbin) for *"achieving outstanding results in a difficult time for the country"* and the achievements in T-60 production at Plant №264 in particular are significant considering the main task of the plant to deliver T-34 hull and turrets sets to STZ.

After what can be best described as a difficult start to se-

Plant drawing of an experimental modernization of the original T-60 turret hatch developed at the KB of Plant №264 in March 1942. Note the large turret ventilator dome and flag hatch on turret hatch. (TsAMO)

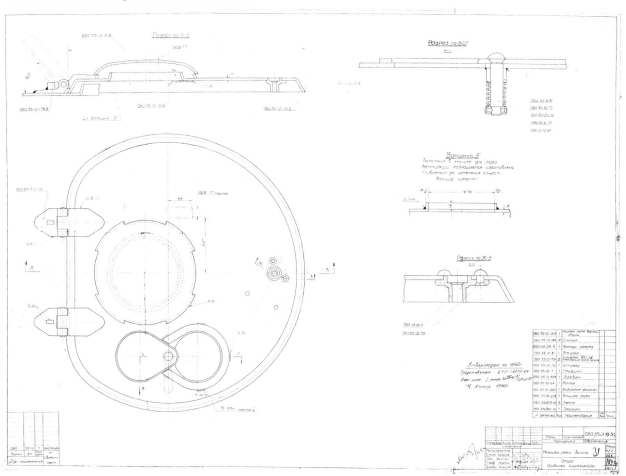

ries production, the supply situation steadily improved in early 1942. The first hull and turret sets finally arrived from Plant №180 in Saratov during the month, and by 1st March Plant №264 had 380 hull and turret sets available, of which 215 were from the "Red October" plant and 70 from Plant №180. In March the output remained only 80 tanks against a target figure of 250 but the availability of hull and turret sets was finally resolved. The supply of components from STZ remained difficult however, with only 35 radiators delivered against a requirement for 350, 170 fuel tanks delivered instead of the 670 required, 133 brake bands as against a need for 1600, and

A T-60 nears completion at Plant №38, in the early spring of 1942. Note the stamped disc roadwheels and the entirely female construction crew in the photograph. (RGAKFD)

only 1257 road wheels (sufficient for 157 tanks) as against a demand for 5000.

Although by March 1942 the adequate supply of hull and turret sets had been resolved, the quality of supply had not. GAZ raised quality claims against Plant №180, but it would seem that a very high percentage of hull and turret sets delivered to Plant №264 had serious cracks in the armour, replicating problems with armour delivered from the Red October plant in Stalingrad.

In the month of March, 35 hulls and 14 turrets arrived from STZ with inherent cracks, while 50% of all hulls and turrets arriving from Saratov had similar faults. As a result, for the period 1st March - 4th April 1942, Plant №264 received claims against 47 tanks delivered to the Red Army.

The problem was such that on 9th April a meeting was held at Plant №264 with representatives of the "Red October" plant and Plant №180, attended by the chief of the 1st Department BTU KA, military engineer 1st Rank I. A. Burtsev. The meeting reviewed the unacceptable volume of cracks, dimensional inaccuracies relative to the drawings, and lack of finishing on the armour, all of which had to be rectified at Plant №264. In particular the gaps and poor edge preparation of the parts prior to welding was highlighted, leading to the requirement for fillets being welded in to close gaps, with an obvious effect on armour integrity.

The meeting resulted in a myriad of manufacturing and quality control changes, not least a decision to stop reworking defective tank hulls and turrets at Plant №264, which was pushed back to the "Red October" plant and Plant №180, which were instructed to stop shipping obviously defective hull and turret sets.

In addition to demands on increased process and quality control, to enforce which a team of engineers would be emplaced at the "Red October" plant and Plant №180. Other changes were to stop hardening "IZ-1" armour in water, and to strengthen the turret, driver-mechanic's "rubka" and other armoured components. Hardness checks were also now to be done in accordance with the established international "Brinell" method. Series production and sub-component supply now being stabilized to some extent, Plant №264 was able to deliver 249 T-60 tanks in the first three months of 1942.

On 16th April, the KB of Plant №264 directed by Frolov as chief designer and with Khodos as chief engineer prepared new specifications for the T-60 hull, turret and the armor layout, which were signed off by Burtsev.

The directorship of the "Red October" plant, as sub-supplier objected vehemently to these changes and complained to Moscow. At the same time arguments took place between the management of Plant №264 and Plant №180 with claims and counter-claims. It transpired that Plant №264 had mixed hulls and turrets delivered from the two sub-suppliers during assembly, with for example 22 turrets from Plant №180 having been mounted on hulls from the "Red October" plant. Parts had also been cannibalized and remounted as required to maintain overall production, such that claims on quality were not always correctly traced back to the supplier. Under the circumstances, the management of Plant №180 claimed that it would be difficult to establish what hull or turret manufacturer should be addressed in the event of issues with scrap rates.

In accordance with GKO Resolution №1571ss dated 9th April 1942, Plant №264 was obligated to deliver 825 T-60 tanks in the 2nd quarter of 1942. 660 of these tanks were intended to be line tanks and the remainder command tanks fitted with a 9-R radio set, at a price of 75,000 rubles and 77,500 rubles respectively. The command tank production remained theoretical, as Plant №264 had no radios to install.

Production at Plant №264 increased as the quality issues with supplied hulls and turrets reduced, and parts availability increased, with 255 T-60s delivered in April against a plan for 250, with Plant №180 rebuilding 9 hull and turret sets before delivery in accordance with its new directive. The "probka" (cork) in the production schedule was now radiators, of which STZ delivered only 190 against a demand for 350. The solution at Plant №264 was to start production of its own radiators.

With the increase in the number of suppliers of hulls and turrets, the appearance of T-60 tanks produced at Plant №264 began to change. The first T-60 tanks produced at Plant №264 in Krasnoarmeisk were almost identical to GAZ production T-60 tanks, the main difference being only the cast road wheels. The plant immediately began production of T-60 tanks with thicker base armour, although a very small number were assembled at the plant with "ekranirovka" screened armour. From the spring of 1942, Plant №176 also began to deliver hull and turret sets to Plant №264 for final assembly. Plant №176 never switched over to the production of thicker base armour, delivering thinner armoured hull and turret sets which were then screened at Plant №264.

The "Red October" plant introduced changes to the hull and turret sets produced there for delivery to Plant №264 in order to simplify production, which resulted in external changes to those T-60 tanks assembled at Plant №264 from "Red October" plant produced hull and turret sets. One of the most characteristic details was the appearance of an octagonal shaped turret hatch, produced in two variants, which became the hallmark of tanks assembled by Plant №264.

The turret hatch was produced in two versions - with the perimeter edges chamfered at 45°, and with a 90° edge, with the turret roof being modified accordingly. In order to reduce the volume of rivets, the hatch mountings were now welded, as were the rain guards over the turret vision slits. The hull was similarly simplified. The central join between the two hull side armour se-

ctions was now (rather crudely) welded rather than riveted, and the air intake on the driver-mechanic's hatch was simplified with a more angular design, of which two variants were also produced.

In the winter of 1941 and early spring of 1942, the KB at Plant №264 developed a project to modernize the T-60, with some changes similar to those adopted by GAZ. The air ventilator dome was relocated from the front of the turret roof to the turret hatch, with a "mushroom" cover, as commonly seen on other tanks.

As for the hull, it became very distinctive. The air intake over the engine was significantly lowered which dramatically decreased the chance of being hit and damaged by stray bullets or shrapnel. In April a new driver-mechanic's vision hatch of cast design was introduced, which integrated the hatch and mounting brackets in a single casting, with 38mm armour thickness.

The modified hull and turret design were approved by Burtsev on 15th April 1942 but did not go into series production apparently due to disputes between Plant №264 and the Red October plant regarding production. Some components of this project did, however, make it onto series production tanks.

Two variants of ZIP (spare parts) containers were developed at Plant №264 in December 1941. The first type "060-21-Sb.12" resembled the small ZIP container developed at GAZ in August 1941. The second, "060-21-Sb.13" resembled the ZIP box used on the T-34. These boxes were installed on T-60 tanks produced at Plant №264 from the spring of 1942, most commonly with the "060-21-Sb.12" container on the right and the 060-21-Sb.13 on the left track guard, though the original ZIP containers also continued to be used.

Another characteristic detail of the tanks manufactured by Plant №264 was the use of cast road wheels with internal amortization. Due to a severe shortage of rubber in the Soviet Union the plant was by December 1941 forced, as were the KBs at all other tank plants, to begin development of road wheels with the minimal use of rubber. The new cast road wheels resembled the return roller with the same diameter as that of the standard road stamped and welded road wheels - 515 mm. Testing of the new wheels was conducted from 3rd to 26th January 1942, during which the test mule T-60 prototype travelled 1502km from Krasnoarmeisk to the village of Beketovka, with 300km travelled on main roads and the rest on ground covered with snow. During the trial some internal wheel hub amortization "half collet" bearings disintegrated, with the solution being implemented based on the test report conclusions, which advised:

"Rollers with internal amortization are a workable design under the following conditions: use of continuous rubber bearings, tack welding the retaining half-rings to the washers of the hub and careful Assembly."

A revised return idler wheel design was also completed in February, slightly later than the road wheels were tested, which also lacked the rubber outer rim, with the diameter of the cast wheel increased to match the 515mm overall diameter of the original type fitted with a rubber rim.

GABTU was not over-enthusiastic about the new road wheels, primarily due to the problems encountered during the trials, and the new wheels were not initially approved. By April however the lack of available rubber was seriously threatening production output of T-60 and also T-34 tanks. In the April report from Plant №264 it was matter-of-fact stated that:

"We do not have roadwheels with rubber rims. The road wheels currently in transit have still not arrived, in view of which, the plant has begun production of road wheels with internal rubber absorption."

In wartime conditions, the management at Plant №264, as at other plants, had done what was necessary to maintain production output, GABTU approval or not. Not all tanks produced at Plant №264 between April and July 1942 had road wheels fitted with internal shock absorption however. Some T-60s delivered by the plant were fitted with cast road wheels fitted with rubber rims, while due to supply problems with STZ from where most road wheels were sourced, the plant also mounted stamped road wheels with rubber rims provided by GAZ. Likewise, not all T-60s were fitted with rimless cast idler wheels, some being also fitted with cast idlers with rubber rims. The net result of these changes was that in the spring and summer of 1942, T-60 tanks left Plant №264 with a myriad of substantive detail differences, according to whatever components were available for assembly on any given day. Tanks were delivered consecutively with up-armoured standard hulls, screened turret armour, road and idler wheels of cast design with rubber rims, or cast with no rims but internal amortization, stamped wheels with rubber rims, standard or Plant №264 designed ZIP boxes, and different driver-mechanic's and turret hatches. Production output was however the goal rather than aesthetic consistency.

In May 1942, Plant №264 shipped 275 T-60 tanks, exactly per plan, but achieved with great difficulty due to a lack of critical components such as radiators. Engine deliveries from GAZ also became irregular, with the plant standing idle for five days in May due to a lack of engines. Lack of rubber rims resulted in the delivery of T-60s with all cast road wheels and internal amortization as described, and as also seen on T-34s produced at the near adjacent STZ plant in Stalingrad, while track supplies were also irregular. In June, despite a lack of radiators and track that month, the plant delivered 311 tanks against a production plan for 300.

A T-60 produced at Plant №38 in the winter of 1941-42. The tank retains the original turret and spoked cast type road wheels. (RGAE)

A column of T-60 tanks being prepared for train embarkation, Plant №38, July 1942. The tank in the foreground, has an "old" style turret with the message "To the Front, for the Defeat of Fascism" painted on the turret side. The tanks, all with later stamped solid roadwheels, are fitted with the rarely seen canvas gun and turret shrouds. A seemingly random T-30 is also to be seen in the column, awaiting dispatch, probably documented as a T-60. (ASKM)

The increased output inspired confidence that the July production target of 325 tanks as announced in GKO Resolution №1880ss dated 5th June was achievable. However, by July 1942 the issue was not production output, but obsolescence. The Red Army now required tanks with better armament and armour to counter the new types of German tanks being encountered on the battlefield. On 3rd July 1942, GKO Resolution №1958ss was issued "On the production of tanks T-34 and T-70" signed personally by Stalin, and reinforced the following day by NKTP Order №499ss, which in part stated:

"1) Directors of Plant №37 (comrade Frezerov), Plant№264 (comrade Kordkner) are from 5th July to halt production of T-60 tanks, but retain some production capacity for T-60 spare parts manufacture.

2) Director of Plant №37 (comrade Frezerov) is to prepare for series production of T-70 tanks and to ensure the delivery in July of 25 T-70 tanks in accordance with the following schedule: First ten days - 5 tanks. Second ten days - 2 tanks per day.

The existing T-60 (parts) inventory give to GABTU as spare parts, and the inventory of T-60 hull and turret sets not useful for T-60 production should be preserved in storage.

3) Director of Plant №264 is released from T-60 production, so as

to use released capacity for production of T-34 tank and diesel (engine) components for the STZ plant.

Note that some of the equipment may by additional order be removed from the plant and transferred to other plants producing T-34 tanks and diesel engines. The remaining T-60 inventory to be used for spare parts, the existing backlog of finished hulls to be preserved in storage.

4) My deputy comrade Goreglyad to immediately travel to Stalingrad and there to establish the scope of cooperation for manufacturing parts for the T-34 tank and diesel engines between the STZ plant and STZ. Machine shop equipment released from T-60 tank production to be used to increase the production of hulls (hull and turret sets) for T-34 tanks."

Despite this turn of events, Plant №264 managed to deliver 51 T-60 tanks in July, before running out of engines from GAZ and tracks from STZ. The last T-60s were completed at the plant on 26th July, with the majority of T-60s completed in July being despatched to the "local" Stalingrad and Voronezh fronts. Some spare T-60 turrets, and perhaps hull and turret sets, from the remaining inventory at Plant №264 were dug in as fixed firing points and would participate in the forthcoming battles that culminated in the Battle of Stalingrad.

Despite all the start-up and supply chain difficulties encountered at Plant №264, in terms of overall T-60 production the plant was second only to GAZ, with a total of 1174 tanks delivered. After the battle for Stalingrad, Plant №264 was renamed Remzavod (repair plant) №264, repairing Soviet built and also captured tanks and armoured vehicles. From 1944 the plant began to produce parts for other plants such as for the large cast gun mantlet for the ISU-152 self-propelled howitzer and later parts for the T-44 medium tank, before returning to civilian shipbuilding after the war.

On 30th April 2011, some 69 years since last tank left plant in July 1942, a T-60 was recovered from the bottom of the river Dobraya in the Volgograd oblast. The tank, destroyed in the winter of 1942 during the Battle for Stalingrad featured characteristics defining it as having been assembled at Plant №264. On 8th August the tank was moved to the "Volgograd Shipbuilding Plant", the former Plant №264 where it was restored in the assembly shops where it had been built almost 70 years previously. It is currently on display at the Battle of Stalingrad Memorial Complex in central Volgograd.

T-60 Production attempts in Uzbekistan

A slightly obscure chapter in the development of the T-60 relates to attempts to assemble the tank in Uzbekistan. On 9th October 1941 GKO Resolution №732ss was issued *"about evacuation of Plant №37, KiM, Podolsk and the Kolomna plant".* The Resolution required the personnel of Plant №37 (producing T-60 tanks), KIM (producing ammunition) and Podolsk (producing T-60 hull and turret sets) to be evacuated to the premises of the Tashkent Agricultural Machine Plant NKOM (Tashselmash) in Tashkent, Uzbekistan by 20th October, with priority given to the move of tank production from Plant №37 and hull and turret assembly from Podolsk. Equipment and personnel located at the Kolomna plant NKTM and involved in T-60 hull and turret set production were to be evacuated to the "1st May" machine building plant NKPS in Kirov, with production to be re-established there by 4th October in accordance with Resolution №732ss. The evacuation of the machine tooling involved in the production of tank components was to start immediately and be completed by 20th October. By this time a reserve inventory of 150 hull and turret sets was to have been completed at the plants being evacuated in order to bridge T-60 assembly requirements during the evacuation, no small task considering the timescale involved.

Only ten days later, on 19th October 1941, and when the relocation detailed in Resolution №732ss should have been completed, Resolution №811ss *"About evacuation of Plant №37, the KIM and Podolsk plants"*, was issued, according to which plants were to be instead evacuated to Sverdlovsk, thereby shelving the plans for evacuation to Tashkent. The subject was however raised again in early November 1941 by the Se-

cretary of the Central Committee of the CPSU(b) of Uzbekistan U. Yu. Yusupov and the Deputy Commander of the SAVO (Sredne-Aziatsky-Voenny-Okrug, Middle Asia Military Region), Major General P. S. Kurbatkin. Their argument was that there were heavy industry plants in Tashkent - namely the locomotive repair plant named after L. M. Kaganovich and the Foundry-Mechanical Plant NKPS - that would facilitate the organization of tank production. GABTU took an interest in this belated proposal, and on 10th November Malyshev as Commissar for Tank Industry (NKTP) reviewed the proposal to organize T-60 production in Tashkent with the head of GABTU K.A. Fedorenko. A GKO resolution on the organization of tank production in Tashkent was subsequently drafted in support of the Uzbek SSR initiative, confirming the organization of T-60 tank production at the Foundry-Mechanical Plant NKPS in Tashkent, with 10 tanks to be completed in the first quarter of 1942, rising to 60 in the second quarter of 1942. The Foundry-Mechanical Plant would transfer from NKPS to NKTP jurisdiction, with the "Kaganovich" locomotive works instructed to allocate additional space to organization T-60 hull and turret set assembly using the machine tooling evacuated from the assembly workshop of the "Krasny Kotelshchik" plant NKTM. Malyshev as NKTP Commissar was to have all technical assembly and plant production documentation prepared by 15th February 1942, with 10 sets of hulls and turrets to be assembled in the first quarter of 1942 and the director GAZ, comrade T. Loskutov, to supply 15 GAZ-202 engines to the Foundry-Mechanical Plant in Tashkent in the first quarter of 1942, and a further 65 in the second quarter. Narkomchermet (the Ministry of Ferrous Metal) was to ensure delivery of armour plate to the plant in line with planned production output and NKV (Ustinov) and GAU KA (Yakovlev) were to respectively ensure the adequate supply of weapons and optics to the Foundry-Mechanical plant in Tashkent, and NKSM the supply of electrical equipment. Narkomelectroprom was meantime to ensure the supply of the 71-TK-3 radio sets beginning with 15 sets to be delivered in the second quarter of 1942.

Despite the paper preparations, the plan to assemble the T-60 in Tashkent did not materialize and on 16th December Malyshev sent Federenko a letter closing out the matter. Reasons cited for the project being considered impractical included the plant not having a sufficient metallurgical and power supply basis, coupled with insufficient machine tooling, and the overall remoteness of Tashkent. The letter concluded that due to lack of experience in manufacturing 20mm armour plate at these plants, the Tashkent locomotive plant should instead concentrate on the manufacture of spare parts for tanks and the repair of railway plant and equipment.

The T-60 commander performed the functions of commander, gunner and loader from within the confines of the particularly small turret. Spring 1942. (ASKM).

Several plants were ultimately evacuated to Tashkent, while the Kharkov Tank School was also relocated to Chirchik near the city, but attempts to start T-60 production in Uzbekistan ultimately came to naught. Having again changed priorities, the Tashkent "Kaganovich" locomotive plant meantime delivered its first armoured train on 12th January 1942.

T-60 Production at Plant Nº38 (Kirov)

With the plan for T-60 production in Tashkent not ultimately being undertaken, a fourth plant was assigned to assemble the tank. Interestingly the plant concerned was not mentioned in the original GKO Resolution Nº876ss *"On the re-establishment of tank plants evacuated from Kharkov, Moscow and Leningrad"*, even though it had since as early as July 1941 appeared as a key supplier of hull and turrets sets for the new T-60. The Kolomensky Mashinistroitelny Zavod named after V.V Kuibyshev, had since its foundation in 1934 manufactured a variety of equipment including assemblies for submarines. Since the beginning of the war the KMZ plant began to build armoured trains, and on 17th July 1941 the plant received instructions to manufacture hull and turret sets for the "030" (T-30). Somewhat confusingly, the KMZ plant never designated the "030" (T-30) as such. Prior to the plant's evacuation KMZ was not involved in

"060" hull and turret production; but in plant documentation what is now known to be "030" (T-30) tanks are referred to as either "T-40 non-amphibious" or "T-60". The KMZ plant began supply "030" (T-30) hull and turret sets in September 1941, being at that time the only supplier to Plant Nº37, which produced the hull and turret of the T-30 tank, with thicker armour than the T-40, and without the propeller cutout in the hull rear.

At the end of September 1941, while preparing for series production of the later "060" (T-60), the KB at KMZ, headed by M. N. Schukin, also developed a cast turret intended to reduce overall tank production time, which could be installed on the T-30 and T-60. With a weight of 311kg, the new cast turret was heavier than the 203kg of the welded type, with a wall thickness of 22-24 mm. Firing tests proved the new cast turret to be invulnerable 12.7 mm DShK machine gun fire at a distance of 100 metres. Plant records show that the plant had produced 14 cast turrets by 29th September with instructions to install them on hulls and ship the hull and turret sets to Plant Nº37 for final assembly. An official note dated 7th October confirms the instruction, but what occurred thereafter is unknown, as Plant Nº37 was evacuated to Sverdlovsk in October, and there is no information regarding tanks with cast turrets being as-

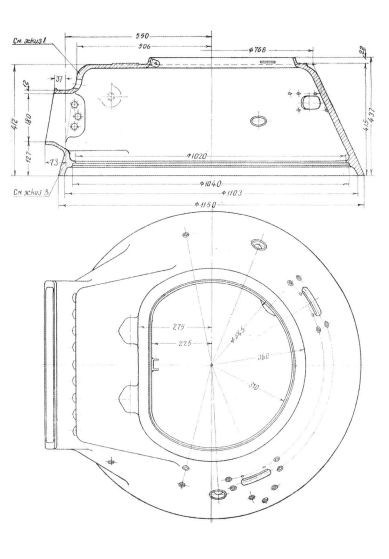

In September 1941, Mikhail N. Shchukin, while chief designer at the KMZ plant in Kolomna, developed a cast turret for the T-30 and T-60. Due to the evacuation of Plant №37 (for which the turret was designed) to Sverdlovsk the turret did not enter series production, though it was probably shipped to Plant №38 to where KMZ was evacuated. (TsAMO)

sembled in Sverdlovsk. In all likelihood the turrets remained in Kolomna and were thereafter shipped to Plant №38 in Kirov.

Planned T-60 production at the Kolomna Machine-Building Plant (KMZ) was interrupted by GKO Resolution №752ss, by which the plant was to be evacuated to Siberia. The partial evacuation of the machine tooling, management and workers of the Kolomna Machine-Building Plant (KMZ) in accordance with GKO Resolution №752ss began by rail in October, with the railcars being sent to the 1st May Machine-Building Plant in Kirov (which bore the same KMZ acronym), and under NKPS control. The new Kirov location had before the war been engaged in the production of railway cranes and similar equipment, not in any way related to the new production expectations of the plant. The Kirov plant area was greatly expanded for receipt of the trainloads of tooling equipment from Kolomna, with additional temporary wooden buildings being constructed for worker accommodation. Production tooling evacuated from Plant №592 (the Mytischi Machine Building Plant) in the northern suburbs of Moscow was also evacuated to the new Kirov plant, with the balance being sent to Plant №37 (Sverdlovsk).

The new combined production facility in Kirov was re-designated as "Plant №38 in the name of Kuibyshev". The director of the plant was initially Ye. E. Rubinchik, who before the war had been director of the KMZ plant in Kolomna, with the chief engineer being Konstantin K. Yakovlev. In May 1942 Rubinchik was moved to Plant №112 where he became director, and Yakovlev took his position as director of Plant №38. Shchukin took over the plant KB, where he would develop several new AFVs, including the SU-76, the largest production self-propelled gun of World War Two, before becoming a designer of steam locomotives after the war.

Engineers at the new Kirov location spent November and December preparing for series production. Plant №38 was originally intended to concentrate on the production of hull and turret sets, for which preparations began in December; however the plant had the industrial capacity to make complete tanks, and the decision was thereby taken to have Plant №38 involved in the assembly of complete T-60 tanks rather than simply produce hull and turret sets for other plants. In addition to T-60 production, Plant №38 had also received several dozen T-30 hulls and turrets that had been evacuated from KMZ in Kolomna, as a result of which the January production target for Plant №38 was set at 200 tanks, including the T-30 tanks, which were assembled on an ad-hoc basis and delivered alongside T-60 tanks as parts to complete them allowed.

The Nizhny Tagil and Chusovoy metallurgical plants were allocated for the production of steel armour plate for T-60 assembly at Plant №38. Roadwheels and other parts were to

A T-60 as produced at Plant №37, as relocated to Sverdlovsk, spring 1942. The hull is up-armoured and the tank has a modified turret with a distinctive sloping armoured fillet behind the gun mantlet. Note the mix of cast spoked and stamped disc roadwheels. (RGAZ)

be provided by STZ, GAZ was allocated engine production, with the rubber road wheel rims to be supplied by the Yaroslavl tyre plant. The contract signed with the Plant №38 agreed a contract price of 75,000 rubles for a fully equipped T-60 line tanks, with no command tanks fitted with radio scheduled for production at the plant.

Plant №38 in Kirov completed its first T-60 tank on 10th January 1942; however full series production was delayed for various reasons. By early February the assembly shop remained incomplete, while the compressor plant, open-hearth furnace, and part of the workshops were not yet operational. The chaos encountered during the evacuation process led to some of the evacuated equipment arriving at Sverdlovsk, Molotov (today Novokuznetsk) and even Kazan instead of Kirov, with the re-routing to Plant №38 taking some time to organize. Further, the production output of tanks at Plant №38 was significantly affected by delivery shortages from key component suppliers. GAZ fell behind in the delivery of engines, and also cast and forged parts. Plant №38 had by 1st February 1942 received only 50 engines, of which only 30 of were fitted with electrical equipment. There were serious disruptions in the supply of other electrical equipment, radiators, ball bearings and other components, such that Plant №38 delivered precisely 4 tanks against a production target of 200 tanks for the month of January, and which were actually T-30s assembled from inven-

tory delivered by rail during the evacuation rather than T-60s.

Production output was also affected by the fact that Plant №38 in January also launched production of M-13 rocket launchers as directed by Malyshev. In accordance with the agreed plan, the plant was expected to deliver 90 M-13's between 15th January and 2nd March, with some 30% of all machine tooling preoccupied with this additional task. The Plant №38 production report for January 1942 showed limited progress with tank production in the main workshops - №3, №5, №6, №10 and №30. The report in part stated:

The plant does not yet have high-quality steel casting and iron forging iron. The forge has insufficient capacity for producing the required output of some components, in particular the required quantity of torsion bars. Production of hulls is down to the plant itself, but the plant has available hulls of the old type. The plant has by 1st February delivered the following"

T-60 (T-40 non- amphibious) (i.e. T-30)	*16 pcs*
"060"	*58 pcs*
Received Turrets	*30 pcs*
Prepared hulls	*150 sets*
Prepared turrets	*48 sets*
Screened hulls	*35 sets*

The report detailed that the plate had not completed the transition to using heavier 35mm glacis armour, while there was no remaining armour plate in inventory. The plant reported to having enough 20mm ShVAK cannon and 7.62mm DT machine guns in stock in order to complete 200 T-60s, but only 70 TMPF sights and a shortage of 20mm armour-piercing rounds and ammunition links. 7.62mm ammunition was not in short supply. The plant also reported that there was a lack of "K.V." engine oil, winter oil and anti-freeze. The plant had only had 45 radiators and 60 batteries available for installation, and the list went on, even detailing that tank assembly was held back by the lack of apparently minor but critical components such as the rubber mounting blocks under the engine. All of which disrupted assembly and acceptance of completed tanks. Plant №38 also instigated in-house casting of track links which had previously been the preserve of STZ production.

Realizing that under prevailing conditions the production targets were unrealistic, GABTU reduced the February production requirement to 75 tanks, with 76 actually assembled that month. The plant had problems with the composition of the armour plate delivered from the Chusovoy metallurgical plant, such that to reduce the high scrap rate Plant №38 was required to carry out the tempering of parts in the water, which in turn led to some of the armour plate warping.

As of February 1942, the main production output of Plant №38 was the T-60; however the plant continued to intermittently assemble T-30 tanks from available components. All tanks produced by the plant were however designated "T-60" regardless of their actual type, such that only analysis of the serial numbers in production records can determine the exact type produced (T-30 tanks produced at Plant №38 had serial numbers starting with a 2). At least ten T-30 tanks were produced alongside the T-60 according to the February shipment records, and intermittently thereafter, with a known total of at least 49 T-30 tanks produced at Plant №38 in Kirov. There is also a high probability that among the T-30s built at Plant №38 were a small number of tanks with cast turrets located at the plant, and some may even have been fitted to the T-60 but to date no photographic evidence has become available to support this.

The likelihood of achieving the March production target of 150 tanks was assessed by the senior military representative at Plant №38, military engineer 2nd rank Kulikov, as "low". This, according to his report was for a number of reasons, not least a lack of adequate power supply in various workshops, but also due to problems with what was described as manufacturing discipline and quality control. Despite his noted concerns, Kulikov personally worked on achieving the maximum output possible, such that Plant №38 by the end of March actually delivered a total of 160 tanks, ten over target, and assembled 174 hull and turret sets against a target of 170. Plant №38 produced 241 T-60 tanks in the first three months of 1942.

Production output was key at a time of outright war for the

This T-60 (p.64, 65, 66), produced at the relocated Plant №37 in May 1942, is in a typical configuration as built at the relocated Sverdlovsk plant until T-60 production was terminated at the plant. In addition to the increased hull armour and new turret configuration, a myriad of changes were made to reduce production time. Note that the previously riveted hull armour join is now electric welded, with the use of riveting, a time consuming process, being minimized. (TsAMO)

survival of the nation, but so also was combat effectiveness at the front line. Accordingly, and precisely at the time Plant №38 had just overcome its T-60 production start-up difficulties, the plant received new orders. On 9ᵗʰ March 1942 the plant was hit with an additional workload with the issue of GKO Resolution №1417 "On organization of production of T-70 tanks at Plant №37 and Plant №38 NKTP" such that in March in parallel with T-60 series production the plant was also obliged to begin preparations for production of the more powerful T-70. During the same month that it had over-achieved its T-60 production target, the plant also produced five of the new T-70 tank hulls, and produced its first two cast turrets, though T-70 series production was continued with welded turrets as the plant lacked sufficient electric power for an electric furnace with the capacity for series production casting.

With the introduction of the T-70 into production at Plant №38 in Kirov, T-60 production at the plant declined accordingly. The production of "small tanks" (i.e. the T-60) peaked in April with 163 T-60 tanks delivered. The T-70 entered full series production at the plant in May, with T-60 production accordingly declining rapidly, with 109 T-60 tanks produced in May as the tank was replaced by the T-70.

According to the Plant №38 military representative's report for June, Plant №38 delivered 22 T-60 line tanks during the month, plus 10 chassis without turrets for installation of

the M-8 MRS. The plant continued thereafter to ship T-60 tanks, albeit in ever decreasing numbers. Some 25 tanks were shipped in July, on train №15258, within which total were nine T-60s and a single T-30 (serial №2071), shipped to the 1ˢᵗ Gorky Tank School. According to surviving records detailing the serial numbers of delivered tanks, T-60s were later dispatched randomly within T-70 shipments, in accordance with parts being available for their completion. The recording of tank production at Plant №38 was however far from accurate. GABTU acknowledged acceptance of 2 T-60 tanks for June, but according to the plant military representative 22 were delivered, 10 of which were without turrets (for delivery to Plant №113 for installation of the M-8), which does not match the records quoted above. When considering the T-30 tanks that were delivered designated as T-60s, and the later occasional shipment of T-60s within T-70 shipments, the exact production output from Plant №38 will never be precisely known. From available records it is known that the plant welded together a total of 567 hull and turret sets from January to June 1942; and delivered between 524 and 535 T-60 line tanks and at least 10 turret-less chassis for M-8 MRS installation.

Though the plant delivery documentation may not have been entirely accurate, the configuration of T-60 tanks produced at Plant №38 made identification straightforward. Externally, tanks built at Plant №38 in Kirov were virtually identical

Note the use of a standard roawheel in the idler position of this Plant №37 production tank.

to tanks manufactured at Plant №264 and at GAZ until the spring of 1942. As with Plant №264 production, Plant №38 T-60s were fitted with cast road wheels. From the spring of 1942, Plant №38 built T-60s with an upgraded exhaust system with the exhaust pipe mounted over the rear engine deck and fitted with a silencer, but this modified system was not however installed on all tanks.

Simultaneously with the introduction of the new exhaust with silencer, T-60s built at Plant №38 in Kirov began to appear with stamped disc road wheels delivered from GAZ, but the return rollers remained of cast design. Plant №38 produced hulls and turrets with both the thinner base armour and "ekranirovka" shielding, and with thicker base armour.

T-60 Production at Plant №37 (Sverdlovsk)

GKO Resolution №876ss "On the re-establishment of tank plants evacuated from Kharkov, Moscow and Leningrad" also touched on the fate of Plant №37 where the T-60 was originally designed. In accordance with the decree, Plant №37 together with the Moscow KIM vehicle plant were to be relocated to the Sverdlovsk rail wagon repair plant, located beyond the Ural mountains separating European Russia from Siberia. Machine tooling evacuated from Plant №592 "MMZ" (Mytischi) was meantime split between Plant №37 (Sverdlovsk) and Plant №38 (Kirov). The combined machine tooling, engineering staff and their families from three evacuated plants thereby ar-

rived at the Sverdlovsk rail wagon repair plant over the week 28th October to 6th November 1941, just as the coldest winter in many years began its icy grip. The new combined plant was designated Plant №37 (Sverdlovsk), with G.S. Surenyan as the Chief Engineer, later replaced by N.A. Popov.

V.A Malyshev (People's Commissar of Tank Production - NKTP), and the Chairman of the Sverdlovsk Regional Committee of the CPSU(b) V. M. Andrianov were tasked to within five days organize an additional 10,000m² of production space and accommodations for the evacuated employees of other enterprises. The plant was ordered to produce its first 5 tanks in November 1941 and 150 in December, by 20th January 1942 to complete the installation of machine tooling, and from 1st February to increase production to 10-12 tanks daily. Simultaneously with the Plant №37 and KIM, the Ordzhonikidze plant in Podolsk was also evacuated to Sverdlovsk. The "Metallist" rail wagon repair plant in Sverdlovsk was tasked at its new location with assembling and delivering T-60 hull and turret sets, to deliver its first 50 hull and turret sets in November, 200 sets in December, and to deliver 12 hull and turret sets daily by 15th January, with the remaining machine tooling to be installed by 20th January.

As in the case of Plant №264, the timeframes specified in the resolution were unrealistic. All of November and part of December was spent on setting up production at the new location. On 19th December GKO Resolution №1043ss was issued "About the plan of production of tanks in the first quarter of 1942" according to which the Plant №37 was expected to produce 700 tanks in the first three months of 1942, including 140 command tanks fitted with radio. According to the contract signed with the plant, the cost of a T-60 line tank was set at 72,500 rubles, or 75,000 rubles with radio installed. The plant was in late December in reality entirely unready to start T-60 series production. The state of affairs at Plant №37 to 25th December 1941 is evident from the Memorandum of the assistant to the military representative of BTU KA military engineer 2nd rank Minin:

"1. In accordance with its resolution, the government required production to start at the plant by 1st December this year, with delivery of 160 tanks in the month of December. The resolution was not carried through. On 25th December, 11 tanks were delivered, which were accepted (for service), and no new hulls were manufactured. The assembly line as of today has used up the inventory of hull and turret sets delivered to the plant, and as of 25th December there are in various stages of production: T-40 - 137 tanks, T-60 - 45 tanks, and repaired and returned for assembly 27 T-40 hulls. There are also 110 turrets in production, of which 25 do not require further machining.

2. Plant output was calculated at up to 35 hulls (hull and turret sets) per day. The status of equipment installation as of 25th December is as follows:

• Preparation workshop. There are 8 "Grisheim" machining centres, 3 of which are now in operation, with electric motors being installed in the others. Preparation work for the installation of "Thomas" shears is underway and a large and small guillotine have been installed.

• Thermopress shop. 6 hardening, 4 annealing and 9 standard furnaces are being completed in accordance with the plan, as is scheduled delivery of 3 presses of 750, 400 and 200 tonne capacity. The 400-tonne press has now arrived at the plant, the rest are still en-route.

• Machine shop. 35 machining centres are now installed in the small parts department, against a plan for 37. 35 machine tools are installed in the large (component) machining centre department against a plan for 58. To 25th December this year not a single rotary machining centre has been installed. This was the result of delays in the dismantling of the old equipment and a lack of tractors at the plant for moving machine tooling.

• Hull assembly shop. The workshop is basically equipped as required. There are some issues, the compressor is delayed, which makes it impossible to perform riveting, preparation works are being undertaken on the installation of a crane on the site of final hull and turret set delivery. Foundry. Provides the plant's requirements for iron castings. Steel casting and ductile iron is provided in cooperation with in Chelyabinsk and Uralmashzavod plants. In early 1942, the construction of slow furnaces for the production of ductile iron is expected. The oxygen station building is being completed, with oxygen and acetylene being temporarily imported to the plant.

The report then listed the entire inventory of steel armour plate located at the plant as of 19th December, which consisted of 4mm (52 tonnes), 6mm (43 tonnes), 9mm (73 tonnes), 10mm (201 tonnes), 13mm (130 tonnes), 15mm (633 ton-

A destroyed T-60 produced at Plant №37 in the early spring of 1942. The hull armour plates are of riveted construction.

nes), 20mm (58 tonnes), 25mm (14 tonnes). The original Soviet document lists the weights to the very last kilogram.

The report indicated that steel armour plate would be provided by the Chusovsk and Vyksa (Vyksunsky) plants, and listed the critical areas for concern as within the preparation workshop, specifically delays in the installation of guillotines and presses, a lack of vertical lathes, and of acetylene gas for cutting and welding. As regards changes to the T-60, the report further stated that the drawings for the up-armoured (ekranirovany) T-60 with 35mm armour on the glacis, driver-mechanic's "rubka" sponson and forward turret armour were now complete. Minin concluded his report with the statement that:

Chairman of People's Commissariat of the USSR Comrade Malyshev has allowed the assembly of an additional 100 hulls (hull and turret sets) without "ekranirovka".

The plant was able to deliver 22 tanks in December, of which 2 (two) required rework before acceptance by the Red Army. Due to a lack of 20mm TNSh armament, the first 5 T-60s were delivered armed with the 12.7mm DShK. There is some conflation in source material with regard to what the "first batch" of T-60 tanks actually comprised of. The 45 "T-60" tanks referred to in Minin's report as being in production at Plant №37 in Sverdlovsk as of 25th December 1941 were in fact tanks being assembled using T-30 and perhaps also T-60 hulls evacuated from Plant №37. The T-60 was not assembled at Sverdlovsk in December 1941, nor in January 1942, as the re-established plant began assembly using inherited inventory of up to 200 T-30 and T-60 tank hulls evacuated to Kirov from the aforementioned plants. Some 101 of these hulls (hull and turret sets) were fitted with "ekranirovka" additional armour screening.

In January 1942, the plant was visited by military engineer 1st rank I. A. Burtsev, who was tasked with reviewing manufacturing capabilities and assisting in the organization of hull production. According to his report, as of 12th January some machining centres were still en route and Plant №37 had not at that time commenced "060" hull production. His report entitled "Production capability of the plant to produce T-60 hulls" advised that:

"In January the plant concentrated on completing T-60 hulls made in Podolsk and repaired the hulls to the specifications as (produced by) the Podolsk and Kolomna plants. 146 of these hulls were completed in January. In various stages of manufacture are T-30 hulls (25), T-60 hulls (87) (where the T-30 is a modified non-amphibious T-40, the T-60 is a simplified hull without

cutout*). Production capability to assemble the T-60 is not ready. Because of this, emphasis is (currently) on T-30 production.

The report went on to review production bottlenecks, which ranged from a lack of rail track within the plant for moving steel plate and completed hull and turret sets, cranes and hydraulic accumulators for the presses not yet having been commissioned, and a lack of compressors and cranes in the final assembly shop, while the plant production layout was not as efficient as it might be. The net result was that in a best case scenario the plant could produce 200-300 hull and turret sets monthly, as the limited assembly areas prevented better output.

A list of decisions taken by Burtsev for implementation at the relocated Plant №37 for 1942 production followed, which included armour thickness (glacis and frontal armour - 35mm, side armour - 15mm, rear armour - 15mm, roof armour - 15mm, floor armour 10mm at the front and 6mm at the rear and two turret options, rolled armour plate 35mm and cast turret 35 - 40mm, with a cast mantlet 35-40mm thick. With these armour thicknesses the hull had a weight of 2348kg, the faceted welded turret adding 540kg, and the proposed cast turret 488kg, with the overall hull weight compared to the "T-40 (non-amphibious)" (i.e. the T-30) being 200kg heavier and the turret weight being increased 284kg in the case of the faceted rolled plate armour turret, and 234kg for the proposed cast turret. The combat weight of the modified T-60 for production at Plant №37 from February 1942 was 6200kg.

The production drawings for the "ekranirovka" (shielding) of the T-60 hull (actually the hull and turret) specified that the hull including the "rubka" or driver's "cabin" would be constructed from 15mm and 20mm armour sheet for a total thickness of 35mm. The turret would be similarly constructed of 15mm base armour with additional 20mm screening, also for a total of 35mm. There followed a statement ominously headed "about the plant management" which reported that:

1. Factory Director comrade Frezerov energetically and technically competently manages the plant.

2. Chief engineer comrade Martirosov has absolutely no idea about tank production. Technically (he is) very weak and therefore has no authority.

3. Another weak point is the lack of a substantive chief designer. Though appointed, comrade Postnikov is not capable of performing this responsibility.

4. All questions regarding armour production are decided by the deputy chief engineer of the plant, comrade Svet, who has authority among the workers.

---

* It is clear from description from the plant military engineer assigned to the project why the T-30 and T-60 are often confused in production reports as even he considered the T-60 as a simplified variant of the amphibious T-40.

Guards Tank Commander Lt. Sabanin and "nachalnik boepitanya" (armourer) Guards Lt. Volkov, loading the 20mm TNSh armament of a T-60 of the 30th Guards Tank Brigade, Leningrad Front, summer 1943. Note the extended turret frontal superstructure specific to Plant №37 (Sverdlovsk) production tanks, and the turret hatch ventilator housing. Wartime photographer V. Tarasevich (RGAKFD)

I believe it is necessary to put the question before NKTP about replacement of the Chief Engineer and Chief Designer of Plant №37, as Chief Engineer comrade Martirosov and Chief Designer comrade Postnikov cannot provide implementation of the plant production program."

T-60 production finally began at Plant №37 Sverdlovsk in the mid February 1942, the relocated Plant №37 thereby becoming the final enterprise to begin assembly the tank type. The plant managed to assemble 147 tanks in February (of which only 67 were T-60s) and also assembled 125 hull and turret sets. The working conditions at the relocated Plant №37 are evident from the February plant report, which in part stated:

"The inability to fulfill the tank and tank hull (and turret) production plan is due to the following reasons:

1) Transfer from T-30 to T-60 tank production. At the moment of transfer, the plant was not fully ready. Some 150-200 new parts were not ready, and the plant had to literally manually produce these parts, which affected tank production output.

2) The Lack of assembly space for tanks and hull and turret sets, as well as the lack of a specified test area for production acceptance. If in December-January the plant had enough space, in February and March it was insufficient, and the plant is choking in the final assembly and final acceptance spaces. Tens of tanks stand outside in the frost. The plant has nowhere to arrange delivery of tanks. The builders have already failed their fifth (consecutive) target date for commissioning of the assembly shop buildings, test area, pump station buildings etc. Now for the sixth time, the builders promise to complete and hand over these premises in the month of March. The quality of construction is shockingly bad, the foundations under the machine tools (lathes etc) and presses crumble or crack. Wooden floors, laid on the frozen ground in the machine shops, bend under the machine tools, it being necessary to move them to other places. The builders are building awfully slowly, with poor quality of execution, all of which has been reported to the People's Commissar of Tank Production (NKTP) comrade Malyshev, People's Commissar for Construction (NKSP) comrade Ginzburg and comrade Malenkov.

3) The Plant has recently received about 3,000 unqualified workers, all distributed through the workshops and the plant has only begun to teach them production. 43% of the workers require to be trained in different specialties at the plant, this has also affected the production of tanks and hull and turret sets during the month of February.

4) Terrible work of sub-suppliers. Plant №183 and the Kirov plant again disrupted the supply of steel armour plate and ductile iron, as well providing poor workmanship. Tank assembly is frustrated by the lack of road wheels, spark plugs, batteries, etc.

5) Idle time of machine shops. Up to 30% of the equipment stands idle on some days due to the lack of forgings, stampings and castings. The mechanical workshop worked much better in the month of February than in January. Today the plant has a good inventory of parts and assemblies (for up to 30-40 tanks), and delivery of spare parts to the fronts has sharply risen. In December spare parts delivery (against plan) was 0%, in January 6% and in February 58%. The plant has every expectation to reach 100% in March.

6) Unsatisfactory performance in hull and turret set production, Assembly of tanks at the end of February decreased due to the fact that hull and turret production started to provide only 4-5 sets daily, which greatly reduced overall tank output. The plant has now used up the reserve hull and turret inventory delivered from Moscow, and the plant did not receive new hull and turret sets in February.

There is a danger that in March the plant will not be able to receive from hull and turret production the number of hull and turret sets required to meet tank production targets. The plant takes all measures to ensure delivery of 8-10 hull and turret sets daily in the month of March, but at the same time, so as not to disrupt production, asked NKTP to send from other plants 100-120 hull and turret sets that will help the plant execute the (production) program. In view of poor performance by sub suppliers, the plant is taking precautionary measures to get rid of them.

At the end of February, Plant №37 received the first batch of its own malleable iron, and by use of its now commissioned slow furnaces in the thermo-press shop obtained the high quality required.

On 3rd March, the three slow furnaces were completed, which made the plant relatively self sufficient in terms of malleable iron for production output. The plant also concurrently started its steel casting, albeit in small quantities.

With commissioning of the new electro-furnace, the plant will have its own steel castings, except the road wheels and tracks that need to obtain elsewhere.

In March the plant will have more assembly areas, warehouses, a test area, pump station etc., as well as mastering its own malleable iron casting, steel casting, etc., in order to gain full capacity for the transition in April-May to the full series production of tanks."

Plant №37 after a slow start to the year produced an estimated 515 "T-60" tanks in the first three months of 1942, including an unknown number of T-30 tanks assembled and shipped as T-60s. In theory, everything was coming together for stable production output from Plant №37. However, this changed dramatically due to the release of GKO Resolution №1417 "On the organization of production of T-70 tanks at Plant №37 and Plant №38 NKTP issued on 9th March, in accordance with which T-60 production, so painstakingly mastered

A destroyed T-60 on the Volkhov Front. The tank was produced at Plant №37 in the spring of 1942. The photograph gives a good view of the hatches, including the simplified driver-mechanic's hatch. The tank is missing its main armament.

at the relocated Plant №37 was to cease forthwith in lieu of organizing production of the T-70 developed at GAZ. The T-70 was clearly better armed and armoured that the T-60; however having significantly struggled to establish T-60 production the plant was simply not ready to convert to the production of a more complex tank.

The People's Commissar for Tank Industry (NKTP), Malyshev, was, and not for the first time, forced to directly intervene. On 9th April 1942, Molotov had on his table a memorandum from Malyshev, which read:

"In accordance with GKO resolutions dated 6th and 9th March this year, the GAZ plant, Plant №38 and Plant №37 are moving in April and May of this year to the production of T-70 tanks. Now it has turned out that:

1. The design of the T-70 has not yet been completed and thereby nor have the final drawings.

2. The number of new parts for the T-70 compared to the T-60 tank, has turned out to be more than first thought, so production preparation requires more time than considered in the GKO decision.

3. Development and delivery of related products (electrical equipment, metal, etc.) has also delayed the timing. All of this threatens to disrupt the timing of development and production of T-70

tanks, especially at Plant №37, having poor communications with GAZ, which plant is at the same time phasing out T-60 production. As a result, the army may not receive the required number of tanks in the time required.

Therefore I believe that it would be correct to maintain the purpose the of GKO resolution about T-70 production at GAZ and Plant №38, but for Plant №37 to have a reprieve for three months and to continue production of the T-60 (during this time). In this case the army will receive another 400 T-60 tanks.

And only after GAZ and Plant №38 have begun full series production of the T-70, to move over to the production of the T-70 at Plant №37.

Molotov on 10th April conferred with Federenko and Akopov, the result being approved as GKO Resolution №1581 dated 12th April 1942:

In a partial amendment of GKO Resolution №1417cc dated 9th March this year, the State Defense Committee (GKO) decides:

1. To oblige Narkomtankprom - comrade Malyshev and Director of Plant №37 - comrade Frezerov to continue production of T-60 tanks, simultaneously carrying out preparation for the production of T-70 tanks.

The production schedule for T-60 and T-70 tanks at Plant №37 was set as follows:

	April	May	June	July	August
T-60	230	280	300	200	100
T-70	-	-	-	10	75

The Resolution further obliged comrade Akopov at Narkomsredmash (NKSM) to ensure the production and supply of GAZ-202 engines to Plant №37 Narkomtankprom, complete with carburetors and electrical equipment, in accordance with the above production schedule, with the delivery of "paired" engines for the T-70 starting in July. The Resolution was personally signed by the chairman of the GKO, Iosef Stalin. Although Plant №37 had received a small reprieve, numerous problems remained, not least related to other plants in the supply chain. 165 tanks were delivered to the Red Army in March; however, although 190 T-60 tanks were produced in April, of that total 86 were without tracks. GAZ had now reached preeminence in ensuring non-delivery of tanks, with a delivery shortfall of 664 engines in the first three months of 1942. Due to engine supply issues, the assembly shop of Plant №37 was idle for 8 days during the month of April. The plant had assembled 230 hull and turret sets, exactly on plan, in April, so the delay in engine deliveries over which Plant №37 had no control had a major effect on T-60 deliveries from the plant. The forecasts regarding the volume of production of tanks in May were bleak:

"The plant is ready to implement the (production) plan, but the plant sub-suppliers prevent the plant from operating, every month there is significant downtime due to poor supplier performance. The May plan may be thwarted just as the April plan was, because of the failure of engine deliveries.

In the first days of May the plant stands idle due to a lack of engines and looks like it will stand idle for a long time. The People's Commissariat does not help the plant, there is no track in the plant, and no perspective of receiving any. Approximately 100 tanks currently stand complete but awaiting tracks. The People's Commissariat has undertaken no measures. The plant needs help. The Director sent several telegrams to comrade Molotov requesting help for the plant. The plant has thereby resolved to do everything in-house. The plant has developed its own malleable cast iron production. It has mastered the fitting of rubber rims on road wheels, and has recently embarked on installing a 5 tonne electric furnace for making its own castings, including track. The plant is working on the in-house production of water radiators, such that the plant thereafter requires from other sub-suppliers only engines and bearings.

During acceptance runs, the majority of defects are related to the engines. The hull (and turret) armour is without cracks due to the correct application of heat treatment. Hulls are accepted only with "ekran" (additional shielding), the faceted turrets likewise only with "ekran" shielding.

In service the tanks perform well, as does the "ShVAK" gun, with defects being fixed before the tanks leave the plant. Claims from combat units are primarily related to engine defects.

In view of the fact that the engine supplier is far from the plant (about 2000km) and the poor situation with the engines, I request your intervention with the chief of GABTU KA about installing the ZiS-5 engine in the T-60, this engine now being made in the town of Miass. In May this plant (i.e. the ZiS plant) can deliver the first 100 engines. Installing the ZiS-5 engine in the T-60 requires some rework but the engine will work better than the (GAZ) 202 engine, and receiving engine deliveries from the plant will be easier than from GAZ."

This was the second occasion whereby GAZ had failed Plant №37 with the supply of GAZ-202 engines, which had been a consideration at the time the T-60 hull design was being finalized at Plant №37 in its original location in July 1941.

ZiS-60

As was obvious from the above-cited Plant №37 production report for May 1942, the lack of delivery of GAZ-202 engines from GAZ was a critical factor in slowing the output of completed T-60 tanks. The installation of a modified ZiS-5/ZiS-16 engine was therefore a potentially critical design change. Development work on the ZiS-5/ZiS-16 engine installation for the T-60 was led by Department №22 within the Plant №37 KB which was at the time led by G. S. Surenyan, who was replaced by N.A. Popov (who had earlier worked on the earlier T-40) in the role in the spring of 1942.

The only spare engine available at the time was removed from a ZiS-16 bus, which had covered 35,000km without an overhaul. This was used for initial tests, later substituted by the "correct" ZiS-16 engine, with the prototype tank installation being designated ZiS-60 by the ZiS plant. Compared to the standard ZiS-16 engine the prototype developed for the T-60 had a modified exhaust manifold, flywheel housing and engine mounts, a crankshaft pulley driven fan drive and a larger radiator. The main final drives were also modified on the prototype test tank, as was the exhaust system.

The tank began trials with the duly installed new engine proto-type on 19th May, with the tank loaded with weights to simula-te a design combat weight of 6800 kg, while the Plant №37 KB worked on modifications required to the tank hull. The results of the tests completed on 9th July showed that the engine worked at lower revs compared to the GAZ-202, with a speed equal to the standard tank (actually 1km/h higher). It was also observed as quieter running. Cooling was noted as being inadequate, though this criticism also related to the standard GAZ-202 installation in the T-60, while access for maintenance remained acceptable. The idea to install the ZiS-5 and ZiS-16 (ZiS-60) engine in the T-60 was accepted, and five tanks were to be built for full evalu-ation. Though several modified ZiS-60 hulls were apparently manufactured by the relocated "Ordzhonikidze" armour plant evacuated from Podolsk, only the single prototype was comple-ted and series production did not ensue.

Even before beginning experimental work on the ZiS-16 engine, Department №22 undertook experimental work on the T-60s running gear, in some cases replicating solutions consi-dered by GAZ in the late winter and early spring of 1941-42. One such development was the development of track exten-sions for use in deep snow. Department №22 in January 1942 developed removable track extensions of forged construction, which were bolted to the standard track as required for use in winter operations. According to the design specifications the-se track extensions (not to be confused with grousers) were developed to aid movement over snow covered roads and ground, to aid turning, and to prevent packed snow build up on the drive sprocket. The extensions were mounted on all track links, greatly reducing the ground pressure from 0.5 kg/cm² to 0.26 kg/cm² even though the combat weight had increased from 5720kg to 6080 kg. Tests conducted from 27th March to 7th April 1942 showed that the tank could traverse an additio-nal 30cm depth of snow with the extensions fitted, for a 10% loss in speed. The design was however considered unreliable, as 73 extensions were damaged during trials covering 150km. The test results required development of a modified design, but this was never completed.

Development work on track extensions was far from an academic exercise. Received wisdom indicates that the T-60, as with the T-40 and T-30, had good tractability on snow due to low combat weight. A report from the BTiMV section of the 20th Army regarding the use of tanks during the winter of 1941-42 suggested otherwise:

"T-60 - maneuverability is very limited. The narrow tracks cut through snow to the ground, so the tank sits on its hull floor. The depth of snow the T-60 can override is not more than 30 cm, over rough terrain - 20 to 25 cm.

The conclusion on the usage of T-60 tanks is:

a). Operation use of tanks of the 20th Army showed that in the pre-sence of 30-40cm snow cover the T-60 can only move on made roads. Severe frosts lead to (the need for) frequent warming up of engines and (therefore) high fuel consumption. The occasional warming (of engines) is not a viable option, as the radiator water freezes.

b). It is advisable to use tanks in areas with less snow - in the south. In the districts of Moscow the snow cover is great and the T-60 cannot be used to support infantry in the attack, or for the de-fense of settlements, headquarters, etc."

In addition to the track extensions, alternative road wheels were also developed at Plant №37 in Sverdlovsk. In the mid March 1942 a T-60 prototype was tested fitted with balancing arms fitted with all-steel small (280mm) diameter road wheels in lieu of the standard 515mm road wheels. This design, develo-ped under the leadership of the running gear group at Depart-ment №22 led by R. A. Anshelevich, replaced the requirement for rubber rimmed road wheels at a time of wartime shortage of rubber in the Soviet Union, while also improving the tank's ground pressure. In order to install the balancing arms on the tank the ground clearance was raised to 380mm, while in-creasing the length of track on the ground from 2203mm to 2530mm decreased the ground pressure to 0.47 kg/cm2. Tri-als were not encouraging however. On the first test, the front right wheel balancer arm unit overturned after 300m of travel; on the second attempt the rear left unit overturned after 200m. The cause of these problems was determined as being the high position of the axis of swing of the bogie combined with the small diameter wheels. The project was duly filed.

The Plant №37 KB a also designed a cast turret for the T-60 in the beginning of May under the supervision of the chief of the hull design bureau G. S. Karapetyants, who had been chief of the SKB (special design bureau) at the Ordzhonikidze plant in Podolsk pre-evacuation. One of the key considerations when developing a cast turret was that it gave the plant in-hou-se capability - also translated as independence from other and unreliable sub-suppliers.

The turret was cast from M3-5 (44-S) grade steel, with the first prototype, with an armour basis from 26-31mm, being tested on the test polygon of Plant №8 from 16th May against fire from the 12.7mm DShK and 45mm anti-tank guns. Test results showed that the turret was immune from 12.7mm fire above 50m range; the results of 45mm fire are not recorded but can be assumed to have been less encouraging. As a result of the tests, it was recommended to replace the standard welded T-60 turret with the new cast type, but the cast turret did not progress beyond prototype stage.

In addition to all the ongoing experimental work on the T-60 at Plant №37 in Sverdlovsk, the plant KB also made several modifications to the production T-60 tank. Until May 1942, T-60 tanks produced at Sverdlovsk differed little from tanks produced at Gorky, Kirov and Krasnoarmeisk. However, design changes were introduced at Sverdlovsk from May 1942 that markedly distinguished T-60 tanks produced at the plant thereafter from tanks produced at other plants. Most distinctively, the tank received a new turret, based on development work carried out at the KBs of GAZ and Plant №264. The frontal section of the turret roof behind the gun mantlet was extended, the additional turret fillet being distinctively sloped. The turret front ventilator (which was never fitted with a fan) was moved to the turret hatch, which was now constructed of roughly finished flat armour sheet, rather than being stamped as before, and was protected by a welded splash strip. Welding replaced riveting on items such as turret hatch hinges and observation slit covers, simplifying manufacture.

A significant amount of changes were also made to the hull and chassis. Like the "Krasniy Oktyabr" (Red October) plant, Plant №37 tried to minimize the use of riveting. The hull side armour sections were welded rather than bolted, and the driver-commander's hatch made of simple flat plate steel rather than stamped as before. The simplified rear stop-light was now an automobile type and moved from the rear of the tank to the hull roof behind the turret. The hulls and turrets of tanks produced at Plant №37 in Sverdlovsk were overall of particularly rough external appearance, though this had no effect on their combat capability.

Plant №37 also introduced running gear of simplified construction. The plant introduced cast road wheels and idler wheels, all of identical diameter for ease of production. The drive sprocket was now a single piece unit (without a removable sprocket ring), with the number of holes latterly increased from two to four.

Work on production modernization was undertaken at Plant №37 in parallel with design work on simplifying assembly of the tank. As with T-34 plants, Plant №37 developed automatic welding, greatly increasing the production rate for hulls and turrets, while increasing quality consistency, with all road wheel production now also being in-house. In May the plant cast its first trial sets of tracks, with series production expected by the end of June. This was particularly important, as Plant №183 was far behind schedule with planned delivery of track for the T-60, and furthermore representatives of Plant №183 had explicitly stated that the plant also had no intention to cast tracks for the T-60, as T-34 production took priority at the plant, and due to high casting scrap rates with T-34 track at the plant, some 40 T-34 tanks were already standing idle ready

for delivery as of 28th May but for their missing tracks. Plant №37 had to appeal to the leadership of the Sverdlovsk regional committee of the CPSU(b) and the People's Commissariat of the Tank Industry (NKTP), to force Plant №183 to comply with its original obligations to produce tracks for the T-60.

Plant №37 delivered 280 completed tanks and a further 300 hull and turret sets in May, but due to the aforementioned issues at Plant №183, all were without tracks. The plant had also been idle for 10 days in May due to a lack of engines, though after their arrival production output was raised to 20 T-60 tanks a day.

T-45 (T-60-2)

In parallel with later design work to install the ZiS-16 engine in the T-60, which had been initiated under the designation "061" or T-60-1 (ZiS-60) and latterly continued at Plant №37, the KB of Plant №37 had also worked on a general modernization of the tank. The subject was first raised at the meeting of the NKTP on 14th May, when Military Engineer 1st rank S. A. Afonin on behalf of Plant №37 proposed increasing the armour basis to 35 mm and installing a 45-mm gun in the T-60. The proposal was initially rejected on the basis that the result remained a compromise when compared to the new T-70, with regard to armour, power output and speed, while the additional armour weight would increase strain on the single engine, transmission and running gear. The upgrade was considered not worthwhile to pursue; however the meeting minutes included the remark to nevertheless *"test this tank for 200km and send the results to GABTU KA"* with a further comment that in the meantime no further work should be undertaken.

The project was supported within Plant №37 by S. A. Ginzburg, who was at the time also Deputy head of the Technical Department NKTP and thereby had very considerable influence on tank development. Ginzberg had been the principal designer of the earlier T-50 tank, and from April 1942 had been overseeing development of a light assault tank destroyer SAU based on T-60 components at Plant №37, so was interested in prolonging the service potential of the T-60 as far as possible. As had become the norm when dealing with higher level "bureaucracy", at the time the modernized variant of the T-60 was being presented to GABTU KA, the new prototype, which had the plant index T-45, was already largely complete.

The development of the T-45 towards the end of the T-60 production cycle was undertaken at Plant №37 in a last effort to continue T-60 production rather than to develop the entirely new T-70 to production which the plant was reticent to do because launching production of the T-70 would require the plant to produce 545 sets of stamp dies for new components, make 825 adjustments and utilize 2,300 tools to manufacture

A T-60 of Plant №37 construction in transit with turret traversed, summer 1942. The tank has an up-armoured hull and new turret, but retains the original and more complex driver-mechanic's hatch. (ASKM)

1440 new parts. By comparison, the T-45 required only 224 new parts, requiring 104 stamp dies, 175 adjustments and 255 new tools, plus 132 parts, 85 stamp dies 85, 149 adjustments and 433 tools already developed for the T-70. Furthermore, launching the T-70 with its twin engines into series production would immediate require double the engine output to be delivered by GAZ, which was at the time only intermittently managing to fulfill deliveries of single engine installation requirements for the T-60.

 In this difficult situation the attempt by the plant KB to develop a tank with more powerful armour and armament on the basis of the T-60 tank, while retaining the existing chassis and single engine installation was entirely logical.

The main external difference between the T-45 and its predecessor was the use of a significantly modified turret mounting a 45mm M-1938 tank gun and co-axial 7.62mm DT machine gun, with a simplified turret rotation mechanism. The thickness of the turret side armour was increased to 35 mm, matching the level of the T-70.

According to the project, the glacis armour thickness could be increased from 35 to 45 mm, bringing T-45 armour protection on a level with the T-70. The hull was basically unchanged from the standard T-60, the main difference being a new hatch for the driver, which opened sideways. The hull armour protection level was left at the level of the T-60, except the upper nose plate, the thickness of which was raised from 15 to 25 mm.

Because the plant had only a single uprated ZiS-16 engine available, the plant installed a less powerful, but commonly available ZiS-5 engine in the T-45 for trials purposes (the test example having been removed from a truck with 12,000km already travelled), which reduced the maximum speed recoded during trials to 37.2 km/h. In the event of successful tests, the plant expected to initially series produce the T-45 fitted with the ZiS-5 engine, switching over to installation of the ZiS-16 engine once the latter was in series production at the Miass plant. In addition to the new engine, the T-45 was fitted with the main and side clutches from the later T-70 and larger diameter torsion bars were fitted due to the increased combat weight, now close to 7 metric tonnes.

The first phase of testing began with test firing on 20th May, with 7-8 rounds per minute achieved at the halt and 3 rounds per minute on the move. Operating the armament within the enlarged turret was noted as more comfortable than in the standard T-60. The hull roof armour warped slightly under the turret during firing, but despite this, all 25 rounds fired hit the target. On serial production tanks it was planned to replace the TMFP sight with the TOP for the main armament.

Mobility trials were conducted from 6th to 13th June, covering a total of 1505km, with 189km on made roads, 805km on cobblestones, 410km on gravel and 110km on a country tracks. The engine was noted as having to be run at high revs throughout the trials to maintain performance, which would ultimately lead to low engine life, while the cooling fan mount welds cracked twice during the trials. There were also several instances of track damage related to quality control issues at Plant №183, with a tendency to also frequently shed tracks.

The tests were however considered successful, particularly considering the tank was tested on a non-standard ZiS-5 truck engine, rather than its design powerplant, and a well worn one at that.

The full test report on both the ZiS-16 engine powered T-60 and the T-45 was sent to GABTU near the end of June. The T-45 was a definite improvement over the T-60, and had it been developed in early 1942 it would have probably entered series production; however by June 1942 the tank, as with the T-60 armed with the 37mm ZiS-19, was hopelessly outdated compared to the new T-70. The T-45 did however have its day: according to surviving documentation the T-45 was at the end of September 1942 sent to a front line operational Red Army unit.

Further development of the base T-45 design included the Plant №37 "062" initiative, which considered the installation of a 45mm ZiS-19BM (Bolshoi Moshchnosti) tank gun on the T-45 chassis, but this was not developed.

End of Days At Plant №37

Meanwhile, the situation with T-60 production at Plant №37 was critical. The plant delivered 321 tanks in June, but only 109 were accepted for service. The remaining 212 tanks were with incomplete armament and without tracks. Given that the July delivery target was another 200 T-60 tanks the situation with the assembly plant and its surrounding sub-contractor plants was critical. In such a situation it was clear that introducing the delayed T-70 at the plant would be difficult, and there were insufficient supplies of engines and tracks even if the new tank could be quickly readied for production.

Against this background, GKO Resolution №1958ss "On the production of tanks T-34 and T-70" was issued on 3rd July 1942 removing the T-60 from production in order to prepare the T-70 for series production, complications or not. Only 10 T-60s were produced in July as the plant reconfigured for T-70 production, which now included the casting of tracks within the plant, with a planned 5-6 sets to be produced daily by month end. This would not come close to matching production requirements on start-up, and the ongoing problem with the supply of engines, of which the plant would now require two for each T-70 produced.

Meantime, the chairman of the Sverdlovsk Regional Committee of the CPSU(b), V. M. Andrianov, applied to the GKO at the beginning of July regarding the production of T-34 tanks at Uralmashzavod. For the organization of this T-34 production Plant №37 was planned to be included in the composition of the Uralmash plant. The fate of Plant №37 was finally decided on 28th July, with the release of GKO resolution №2120 "On organization of T-34 production of T-34 tanks at Uralmash and Plant №37 NKTP" within which instruction Plant №37 was incorporated into the Uralmash plant. The following day the

first two T-34 tanks had been produced - rather suggesting that again the paperwork was behind the reality - with development of the T-70 now transferred to Plant №38.

Plant №37 as of 1st September 1942 still had 130 tanks in inventory, still awaiting tracks. It was planned to complete these tanks with tracks cast within Plant №37, as there was no hope of receiving any from Plant №183 due to its T-34 production commitments. Plant №37 managed to deliver approximately 50 T-60 tanks during September and October, but thereafter increasing T-34 output curtailed further T-60 completion and production. An interesting insight into the situation at Plant №37 relative to the fate of the remaining uncompleted T-60 tanks there is to be found in a letter from Engineer-Colonel G.Z. Zukher (responsible for the the smooth integration of Plant №37 into Uralmashzavod plant production) to the Secretary of the Sverdlovsk Regional Committee of the CPSU(b) Aleksei P. Panin (responsible to the Regional Committee for NKTP) dated 11th October:

"I can report that there are 80 remaining T-60 tanks located at Uralmashzavod after the elimination of Plant №37, these being stored in the yard of the plant under the open sky. The tanks have been kept in this condition for about 3 months, unprotected from the elements. There is no security in the yard. Tools and parts have begun to be stolen from the tanks.

The leadership of the former Plant №37 did not take the required measures to urgently send these tanks to the front though Plant №37 was responsible for them. To date, the management of Uralmashzavod also did not take any real measures to speed up dispatch of tanks. To complete these tanks 80 track sets are required; track manufactured by Uralmashzavod for the T-60 turned out to be of very low quality and it was not possible to install this track on the tanks. Currently Uralmashzavod is mastering casting tracks for the T-34. It is natural that the plant management does not consider itself responsible for the condition of the T-60 tanks, and does not care about accelerating their despatch. This issue was verbally raised by me before the People's Commissar of NKTP comrade Zaltsman during his visit to the plant. However, some 80 T-60 tanks remain as before at Uralmashzavod. My audit of the armament and other parts showed that the material part is covered with corrosion and I had to clean the gun barrels and replace the grease. I ask you to place the question before NKTP about immediately completing the T-60 tanks with tracks from other plants and sending them to the Army."

Plant №37 records show that as at 1st November 1942, 81 TNSh guns were installed on T-60s at the former plant, with one spare gun in the Uralmashzavod warehouse. The majority of ammunition rounds (20,406 of 22,996) and ammunition links (1,096,420 of 1,136,740) were noted as laying under a tarpaulin in the yard, open to the elements. From this it is clear that Zaltsman had not apparently reacted to Zukher's concerns; however on 13th November, the Deputy head of GABTU KA Major-General of tank forces Boris M. Korobkov sent a letter to V.M. Molotov with a request to investigate the seemingly unexplainable situation. The letter reached Molotov at 13:00, and a reply was received from Zaltsman the same day:

"In your letter dated 13th November this year, addressed to comrade V. M. Molotov on the question of completing the 80 T-60s at Uralmashzavod, I report that Uralmashzavod has taken all necessary measures to complete and assemble the missing tracks on 60 T-60 tanks before the end of November, and the remaining 20 tanks in the first five days of December. NKTP has informed the Deputy Chairman of the Council of People's Commissars comrade V. M. Molotov about these issues."

I. Zaltsman was clearly being highly disingenuous. Only after sending the response letter to Molotov did work actually begin at Uralmash on completing the remaining T-60 tanks at the plant. On 17th November tanks were examined by a commission, which concluded that 10 tanks were without TMFP sights, 16 tanks had rust on the gun barrels (presumably the internal bores but not defined), 21 tanks were without lights, and the list went on, such that completion of the T-60 tanks extended well beyond the arrival of the problematical tracks.

Work proceeded on completing the remaining tanks, but it was periodically hampered for various reasons. In December 1942 the plant managed to complete and send 25 T-60 tanks to the front, another 11 in January 1943, and the final 44 T-60 tanks in February. Russian sources indicate that T-60 tanks were produced at Plant №37 in Sverdlovsk until the beginning of 1943, which is technically correct, but these tanks were the "lost batch" of incomplete tanks that were completed in September and belatedly completed as described rather than new production, T-60 series production at Sverdlovsk having been halted on 5th July 1942. In total, Plant №37 at Sverdlovsk built 1033 (some sources state 1144) T-60 tanks before the plant converted to T-70 production. Plant №37 was the plant that sent the final production batch of T-60s to the Red Army.

Total T-60 production, including the original prototype "060" tank produced by Plant №37 in August 1941, and the batch built by September 1942 at Plant №37 Sverdlovsk but completed with tracks months later, was 5662 (some sources state 5839) tanks, of which the Red Army received 5796, of which the great majority, approximately 4164 T-60 tanks, were built in the first half of 1942. The numbers, all of which are subject to refinement based on additional data that may become available, include T-60 chassis developed for the manufacture of self-propelled gun systems.

The T-60 was a tank produced at several tank plants with varying degrees of prior experience in tank or armoured vehicle production. All the T-60 production plants shared the common difficulty of maintaining tank output with irregular component deliveries from other sub-supplier plants, and in many cases were forced to develop new components and the manufacture of those components in-house and from scratch. All this was achieved against a background of the original T-60 production plants being in danger of being overrun, and having to be evacuated and re-established elsewhere, with the KhTZ tractor plant in Kharkov lost to advancing German forces as it was just beginning series production of the T-60. The production difficulties related to the T-60 were not unique to the T-60, being shared by its larger sibling the T-34. A more challenging background to establishing mass production of what became the third largest production tank by volume in the desperate years of 1941 and 1942 at the beginning of the Second World War on the Eastern Front is hard to imagine.

One of the T-60 tanks restored by the Muzei Tekhniki (Vadim Zadorozhny Museum) near Krasnogorsk in the western suburbs of Moscow represents a tank originally produced by Plant №37 in Sverdlovsk. The up-armoured hull and turret is clearly evident in these current photographs.

Chapter 5

The T-60 In Service and Combat

The T-60 was widely deployed in almost all Tank Brigades and Separate Tank Battalions of the Red Army, and served on all Fronts during the initial months of the war on the Eastern Front. The T-60 was used primarily for infantry support, reconnaissance and command duties, and for towing 57mm ZiS-2 anti-tank and 76.2mm Divisional artillery in combat operations. The tank was also used for training tank driver-mechanics at tank schools and near the front line.

The T-60 was not particularly well documented in combat, though it served on all fronts during the early years of the war on the Eastern Front and was also used in the Russo-Finnish "Continuation War" of 1941-1944. The tank has historically been maligned by some authors as being too light to engage with Wehrmacht tanks of the day, a judgment made primarily from the large number of T-60 tanks destroyed in combat and photographed in destroyed state by Wehrmacht photograph-

ers. In retrospect, the T-60 fared no better or worse than any other Soviet tank type in the dark days of 1941-42. Though relatively lightly armed, the 20mm TNSh cannon was effective against light tanks at typical engagement ranges, while the armour protection was not significantly different to that of comparable Axis tanks, and in contrast with Wehrmacht and other Axis tanks was also heavily sloped over its frontal aspects.

Perhaps the principal contribution of the T-60 was that it was capable of being assembled at automotive and other plants that were not primarily equipped for tank production, with these assembly plants being supplied with pre-built armoured hull and turrets sets by other plants with specific armour plate manufacturing and assembly capability. The T-60 was thereby manufactured by several plants and in significant quantities at the very time when Red Army losses at the front were at their most critical. The T-60 served its purpose, providing additional

A T-60 belonging to the 33rd Tank Brigade enters Red Square, 7th November 1941. (RGAKFD)

tank capability when urgently required, with the overall need for light tanks having been diminished by the time the T-60s successor, the T-70, entered production only a few months later. The T-60 was produced over a relatively short timescale, but a critical one in the survival of the Soviet Union as a nation. Only two battle damaged T-60 tanks are known to have survived the war "intact", which in of itself is an indicator of the critical role that the T-60 played at a time when the Red Army was fighting for its very survival. When the T-60 was paraded (for the first and last time) on Red Square before Stalin on 7th November 1941, enemy Axis forces were at Khimki, only 16 km from the Kremlin in central Moscow. Those T-60 tanks moved directly from the parade to join combat units at the front, where almost all were subsequently lost in action. The contribution of the T-60 should thereby be considered not just as a tank type in of itself, but rather with regard to its overall role at the most critical time of the war for the Soviet Union.

The T-60 is understood to have had its combat debut as part of the 10th Tank Brigade in the region of Poltava, Ukraine, at the end of September 1941 as Wehrmacht and Axis panzer column pushed east past Kiev in the direction of Kharkov where the KhTZ plant was located.

The 48 T-60 tanks that paraded through Red Square on 7th November 1941 belonged to the 33rd Tank Brigade. The tanks, some of which mounted the conical turret developed for the T-30 and T-40 were subsequently deployed during the Battle for Moscow.

The T-60 was used on the Leningrad Front, with one of the better-known units being the 61st Tank Brigade which was formed in the spring of 1942 with 60 T-60 tanks, and partook in the operation to break the Siege of Leningrad together with T-60 tanks within the 86th and 118th Tank Battalions and the 67th Army which spearheaded the forced crossing of the frozen River Neva near Leningrad which was the initial combat operation action in breaking the siege. T-60 tanks were used in quantity during the final operation that broke the Siege of Leningrad in January 1944. At the start of the operation, the 1st Tank Battalion on the Leningrad Front had 21 T-60s, the 220th Tank Battalion had 18, and the 124th Tank Battalion had 5.

The T-60 was engaged on the Southern Front from the spring of 1942, as the Red Army held and then began to force back Wehrmacht and Axis forces in the south of the country. The tank was initially engaged in combat in the regions of Kharkov and Stalingrad, and in areas of southern Ukraine including Crimea. After the Battle of Stalingrad the Red Army began to revert to offensive operations on the Stalingrad, Don and South West Fronts, however few T-60 tanks had survived the ferocious combat engagements of the preceding months to participate in quantity in these operations.

The T-60 was also used in some quantity during the 1941-1944 Russo-Finnish "Continuation War", fought in the Karelian Isthmus north west of Leningrad. During the war, the Finns captured a number of T-60s which were pressed into Finnish service, primarily as training tanks.

In 1945, three T-60s were transferred to the Polish Army, but their fate is unknown.

A rear view of the T-60s of the 33rd Tank Brigade on Red Square during the historic 7th November 1941 parade.

These T-60 photographs are typical of what was available from printed Soviet sources, which contrasts significantly with what has become available from Russian sources in recent years.

T-60 №164, 549th Tank Battalion, 61st Tank Brigade, 67th Army, Leningrad Front, 18th January 1943

Commander: Lieutenant Dmitry Ivanovich Osatyuk - Hero of the Soviet Union

Driver-Mechanic: Sergeant Ivan Mikhailovich Makarenkov - Hero of the Soviet Union

One T-60 tank and its crew have a particularly well-documented role during "Operation Iskra", (spark) which would ultimately break the Siege of Leningrad. The tank crew would become Heroes of the Soviet Union, and the tank would also become one of the few to actually survive the war to become a museum exhibit.

Tank №164 belonged to the 549th Tank Battalion of the 61st Tank Brigade of the 67th Army, Leningrad Front. The 61st Tank Brigade was equipped with T-60 tanks, which had been secretly delivered to the combat area around Leningrad on coal barges. Tank №164 was commanded by Lieutenant Dmitry Ivanovich Osatyuk, with Ivan Mikhailovich Makarenkov as driver-mechanic.

Dmitry Ivanovich Osatyuk was born in the village of Mogilnoe Gaivoronskogo in the Kirovogradsky region of Ukraine in 1917. Having graduated from a local cooperative technical college, he worked as an accountant on a collective farm before joining the Red Army in 1939, graduating from the Syzransk tank school in 1941. After the outbreak of war Lieutenant Osatyuk participated in defensive battles in the region of Dvinsk (today Daugavpils in Latvia) and Lugi (in the Leningrad region). From September 1941 he was assigned to the Leningrad Front where he was involved in many engagements in the environs of the city as Leningrad was encircled and the city endured the infamous "900 Day Siege".

In January 1943 Osatyuk's tank company within the 61st Tank Brigade, all of which was equipped with T-60 tanks, was involved in "Operation Iskra", the operation that would ultimately break the Siege of Leningrad. At the commencement of the operation on 12th January 1943, his T-60 tank company crossed the River Neva under heavy fire and traversed a frozen marsh before reaching the edge of a forest overlooked by the Sinyavinskie Heights just before sunset. T-60 tanks were the only tanks able to perform this operation, as although it was mid winter and the ground was frozen, the frozen layer on the peat bogs was not sufficiently thick to support the weight of heavier tanks without them breaking through and becoming bogged down. Heavier tanks would require considerable ground preparation with the liberal use of birch logs, whereas the light T-60 tanks could "float" across the ground without breaking through the frozen top layer.

Having established a tentative bridgehead, Osatyuk's tanks manouvered into position under cover of darkness in order to support an advance by "morskaya pekhota" (marines) in a dawn attack. During the dawn engagement the following morning, the T-60 tanks under Osatyuk's command were outflanked by three German Pz.Kpfw VI Ausf H Tiger heavy tanks of the German 502nd Heavy Tank Battalion, supported by 500 infantry. As Osatyuk's tanks engaged the enemy infantry, the nearest German Tiger tank opened fire with its 88mm armament on his T-60 tank, which with its 20mm TNSh armament had no capability to engage such an enemy tank even at close range. Lieutenant Osatyuk commanded his driver-mechanic, Ivan Mikhailovich Makarenkov, to reverse back towards the nearby woods where a Red Army artillery battery commanded by Snr. Lieutenant Piotr Romanov had manoeuvred into position overnight and could more effectively engage the heavy German armour. The consequent engagement was latterly described as a series of manoevures whereby Osatyuk's T-60 tank company, pursued by the German tanks, was able to "position" the enemy tanks such that they presented their side armour to Romanov's artillery. Pz.Kpfw VI Tiger №250005 was hit in the engine compartment by a 76.2mm armour-piercing round and was immediately destroyed by fire, while Pz.Kpfw VI Tiger №250006 was hit in the turret then suffered transmission damage, such that it was disabled and abandoned by its crew. The third tank left the scene of the engagement though some early Russian sources stated it was also destroyed. With the German heavy tanks absent, Osatyuk's T-60 tank company then moved forward, engaged and routed the supporting Wehrmacht infantry. It was one of these Tiger tanks that after technical evaluation at Kubinka was on 22nd June 1943 put on display in Moscow's Goky Park as part of a collection of captured and destroyed Wehrmacht equipment.

On 18th January 1943, Osatyuk's tank company accompanied the 123rd Rifle Brigade and supporting artillery forces into "Rabochy posyolok №1" (workers village №1), where, together with elements of the 372nd Rifle Division of the 2nd Shock Army of the Volkhov Front the tanks broke through the encircling blockade around Leningrad. The initial breakthrough was only the start of a prolonged operation against enemy forces that had been dug in around the city since the autumn of 1941. Three days after the events described above, Osatyuk's tank was on 21st January hit and knocked out by shell-fire, and driver-mechanic Sergeant Makarenkov was seriously wounded. Osatyuk pulled his wounded driver-mechanic from the destroyed tank under heavy fire, and dragged him to safety where "medsanbat" (medical battalion) medics could take care of him, before himself taking over another tank and re-engaging in combat.

In recognition of his actions during "Operation Iskra", Osatyuk was on 10th February 1943 made Hero of the Soviet

Union. His driver, Makarenkov was similarly decorated. Only three days after announcement of his award, Osatyuk was on 13th February badly wounded when his tank was hit during another engagement. For five hours a military doctor by the name of Glumov operated to keep him alive, before he was evacuated by air to Moscow (which one must assume was due to his new-found status as Hero of the Soviet Union). Though he survived, Osatyuk's injuries were such that he was declared medically unfit to return to active duty, and he was re-assigned to a staff role in a tank training regiment. After the war, now Captain Osatyuk, graduated from the Higher Tank Officer's School and became a regimental commander in the Kantemirovskaya Tank Division, before returning to Ukraine in 1959 as Military Commissar for the city of Kirovograd, becoming a Colonel (reserve) from 1971. He died in 1999, but his entire life never forgot the name of the military doctor Glumov that saved his life in 1941, as he had himself saved the life of his driver-mechanic Makarenkov only days before.

Makarenkov would outlive Osatyuk. Having also been awarded the status of Hero of the Soviet Union for the same engagement during the relief of Siege of Leningrad in Janua-ry 1943, Makarenkov was medically discharged from the Red Army as a result of his particularly serious injuries received during the engagement on 21st January 1943, and did not further participate in the war. He returned to Lipetsk, where he also lived a long life. He died in 2004.

Their tank, T-60 №164 of the 549th Tank Battalion, 61st Tank Brigade, 67th Army, Leningrad Front, had been destroyed in combat on 21st January 1943. Due to the circumstances of the time, the damaged tank was recovered but not put back into service as more powerful tanks were available to the Red Army by January 1943, and the T-60 was of limited effectiveness compared to heavy tanks such as the KV-1 that was used in relatively large numbers in the Leningrad area. Having thereby survived the war, the tank was displayed in the Museum of the Defence of Leningrad, which opened in March 1947 and functioned until the mid 1950s when it was closed and the exhibits moved. The attached post-war photograph shows Dmitry Osatyuk standing by his wartime T-60 displayed in what would transpire to be a temporary exhibition. After the museum closure the tank disappeared and its fate remains to this day a mystery.

Captain Dmitry Osatyuk, Hero of the Soviet Union, stands beside his tank that was destroyed in combat on 21st January 1943, during "Operation Iskra" to relieve the Siege of Leningrad. The tank was displayed at the Museum of the Defence of Leningrad, which operated from 1947 until being closed in the mid 1950s. (CAKFFD via Bair Irincheev)

The T-60 in Combat, from Contemporary Soviet and German photographs...

A T-60 produced by Plant №37 on the march with turret traversed to the rear, Tula region, summer 1942. The tank has an up-armoured hull and new turret but the older and more complex driver-mechanic's hatch. (ASKM).

A T-60 assembled at GAZ in the early winter 1941-42. GAZ applied chemical paint, including winter white, at the plant. (RGAE)

Front and rear views of the same GAZ-assembled T-60 with its plant applied winter camouflage paint.

Driver-mechanic training on the T-60, spring 1942. These T-60 tanks are of Plant №38 production.

A T-60 of Plant №38 production in the winter of 1942. The winter "whitewash" has been hand applied in the field with a brush.

The T-60 tank turret with its 20mm TNSh armament was a tight fit for the tank commander. (AKSM)

A T-60 crew reloads 20mm rounds for the 20mm TNSh into their boxes, summer 1942. (RGAKFD)

A column of T-60 tanks of the 28th Tank Brigade of the 16th Army near Tula, November 1941.

The lead tank from the same column of T-60 tanks is fitted with the conical turret built at Plant Nº37 for the T-30 and fitted primarily at GAZ to the T-60 after evacuation of Plant Nº37 machine tooling and built inventory to Gorky.

The same T-60 tank column of the 28th Tank Brigade photographed from the rear, with the tank in the foreground being fitted with the T-30 conical turret. Note the gun barrel transit shrouds and the bucket on the track guard.

A T-60 of Plant №264 production belonging to the 2nd Batallion, 3rd Guards Tank Brigade, 7th Tank Corps, accompanying a KV-1 "Voroshilov". The tank has spoked cast roadwheels with rubber rims, an up-armoured turret with cutout round the original vision device, and a simplified fantail exhaust without silencer. Note the positioning of the grille covers on the engine deck and the painted out markings. Bryansk Front, summer 1942.

A T-60 of Plant №264 destroyed during the Battle of Stalingrad. Note the cast road wheels with internal amortization and cast rear idler without rubber rims, similar to T-34 production at the time.

A T-60 of Plant №264 destroyed while in rail transit. Note the up-armoured and enlarged gun mantlet.

A T-60 destroyed in combat being inspected by Wehrmacht officers. The tank is of Plant №264 construction.

T-60 tanks built at GAZ destroyed in the Battle for Moscow in the early winter of 1941. The tank in the foreground has stamped roadwheels, the one in the background cast. These tanks are as paraded on Red Square on 7th November 1941.

A T-60 tank of Plant №264 production destroyed in combat. Note the modified gun mantlet, driver-mechanic's "rubka" and the octagonal turret hatch.

This early production tank was returned to Germany and inspected at Kummersdorf. Note the markings denoting armour thickness. (Tank Museum 3210/E4)

A T-60 of Plant №264 construction destroyed in the summer of 1942. The tank has a welded hull and a mix of road wheels.

A destroyed T-60 built by Plant №37 in the summer of 1942. Note the brake/convoy light on the turret rear, borrowed from the ZiS-5 and GAZ-AA, and installed on tanks at Sverdlovsk from the spring of 1942.

An early production T-60 assembled at Plant №37, spring 1942.

A T-60 as produced at Plant №38 in the winter and spring of 1942. (RGAE)

T-60 commander entering turret, spring 1942. (ASKM)

A T-60 as produced at Plant Nº38 destroyed in combat. The tank has an up-armoured turret and an exhaust with silencer fitted. (RGAKFD)

A T-60 burns in the village of Karmanova, summer 1943.

T-60 of GAZ production in March-April 1942. (RGAKFD)

A Plant №37 production T-60 of the 30th Guards Tank Brigade, Leningrad Oblast, August 1943. (wartime photographer - V. Taragevich)

A T-60 of Plant №37 production towing a 45mm anti-tank gun near Nevsky Pyatachok on the River Neva, during the breaking of the Siege of Leningrad, January 1943. (wartime photographer - V. Taragevich)

A T-60 turret Plant №264 (and likely a T-60 beneath it) installed as a DOT, wood and ground (built) fire point, Stalingrad region, summer 1942.

A T-60 is just visible to the left of this photograph taken at the crossroads of Karelskaya and Torkelli street, Viipuri (today the crossroads of Leningrad and Lenin prospects, Vyborg), 20th or 21st June 1944. The T-60 was used extensively in the 1944 "Continuation War" against Finland. Note also the BA-10 based command vehicle. (TsAKFF St. Petersburg, via Bair Irincheev)

The crew of a GAZ production T-60, 21st Army, Stalingrad region, 1942. The photograph gives a nice view of Soviet World War Two era tanker's helmets. 30th Guards Tank Brigade. (TsAKFF St. Petersburg via Bair Irincheev)

Mongolian Marshal Choibalsan inspecting a T-60 and its 20mm TNSh ammunition, Moscow region, January 1943. Mongolia collected money from its citizens for Soviet T-34s and in January 1943 Marshal Choibalsan visited Red Army units in the Moscow region as part of the handover. (Original wartime photographer (probably) Vsevelod Tarasevich)

Most probably Guards Lt. Sabanin, 30th Guards Tank Brigade, standing on his Plant №37 (Sverdlovsk) production T-60, Leningrad Front. Note the turret hatch mounted ventilator. (TsAKFF St. Petersburg via Bair Irincheev)

A T-60 passing through a breached anti-tank ditch, Nevskaya Dubrovka, on the River Neva, Leningrad Front. The photograph is captioned 30th July 1943. Look beyond the tank to the branchless birch trees in the background, which tell their own story (wartime photographer - V. Taragevich via Bair Irincheev)

Chapter 6

T-60 Variants and Prototypes

BM-8 "Katyusha" MRS (Multiple Rocket Launcher) System

The T-60 chassis was used to mount the 82mm "Izdeliye M-8" (article M-8) "Katyusha" rocket launcher system, latterly better known (post-war) as the BM-8-24, although this designation was not used in the war years. As with its larger sibling, the 132mm M-13, the 82mm calibre, 5000m range M-8 rocket was originally mounted on three-axle ZiS-6 truck chassis, but with the arrival of the autumn "rasputitsa" (roadless season) in September 1941 the roads at the Front turned to mud, making them almost impassable to wheeled vehicles such that other chassis were urgently required. A more pressing concern was that the Moscow ZiS plant was also at the time in the process of evacuation to Miass in Siberia, and the supply of assembled ZiS-6 chassis was thereby also dwindling.

The "Kompressor" plant in Moscow developed tracked versions of the M-13 MRS on the STZ-5 tracked artillery tractor chassis, and the M-8 MRS on the chassis of a turretless T-30, which received the respective plant designations KS-75 and KS-77. The prototype KS-77 successfully underwent firing trials at the end of September, and by November the "Kompressor" plant had completed 24 M-8 installations (including the prototype). On which chassis they were actually built is not entirely clear. The plant production summary reports indicate that only 3 M-8 MRS were mounted on the T-30 chassis, but

Due to the crisis at the time of its manufacture, the BM-8 was poorly documented in service configuration. This retouched illustration is one of few illustrations of intact vehicles. (Soviet Military Review)

Plant №37 records document that 10 T-30 chassis were shipped from there to the "Kompressor" plant in September and 14 in October. Moreover, as of 10th October there were 15 M-8 on the T-30 or T-40 chassis in various stages of completion at the "Kompressor" plant, then undergoing evacuation, of which only three were built on the T-30 chassis. In the confusion associated with plant evacuation, the systems were dispatched documented as M-8 MRS mounted on the ZiS-6 chassis, whatever may have in fact been sent.

Due to the plants associated with M-8 and M-13 production being evacuated, assembly of M-8 MRS on a tank chassis was relocated to Plant №113 (ZFS) in Gorky, with the GAZ "Molotov" plant (also in Gorky) contracted to supply turret-less T-60 chassis for the MRS in accordance with Resolution №889ss dated 11th November 1941.

As the T-30 and T-60 were technically similar, conversion of the latter for use as a chassis for the 12 rail M-8 MRS was not time intensive. The M-8 launcher mounted on its turretless T-60 chassis was slightly different from the truck-mounted version: the traverse was more restricted, and the elevating handle relocated. A flip-up footboard was provided for crew access on the left side, near the idler wheel; and a kickstand to simplify reloading was mounted on the rear of the hull. A small commander's "rubka" was located on the hull roof to the left of the launcher assembly.

The first 20 turretless T-60 chassis for M-8 MRS use were made at GAZ in October 1941, 35 in November and 82 in December. In January 1942 35 chassis were built, 32 in February, 20 in March and 14 in April. Plant №113 completed its first 8 M-8 on the GAZ supplied chassis in November 1941; with two additional systems delivered for installation on armoured trains. In December Plant №113 completed 107 M-8 systems. In January 1942 Plant №113 completed a further 113 M-8, but only 54 of them were installed on the T-60 chassis. Production was limited by the number of available chassis delivered from GAZ and also a lack of sights from Plant №69. In February, output was again limited by a lack of chassis, and production stopped altogether in March, as not a single T-60 arrived from GAZ, the required chassis belatedly appearing in April and May.

The exact number of M-8 MRS mounted on the chassis

of the T-60 at Plant №113 is unknown, and can be assumed only from the number of chassis built. On 9th August 1942, the People's Commissar of Machine Tooling, A. I. Efremov received a complaint that Plant №113 was ignoring the program to produce rocket launcher systems on imported vehicle chassis, and had in July 1942 built only 18 M-8 MRS on tank chassis.

Plant №38 in Kirov also produced 10 tank chassis for M-8 MRS installation according to a production report dated June 1942, though whether these chassis were sent to Plant №113 for MRS installation or completed elsewhere is unknown. M-8

MRS assembled on T-60 chassis built at Plant №38 form the majority of vehicles photographed in wrecked form by Wehrmacht troops in the fighting in the summer-autumn of 1942. No production plant photographic records are known to have survived, such that even in official Soviet handbooks photographs of wrecked M-8 vehicles are shown. In total, Plant №113 assembled 238 M-8 MRS on chassis delivered by GAZ, and 10 chassis were completed based on Plant №38 delivered chassis, for a total output of 248 M-8 MRS vehicles built on the T-60 chassis.

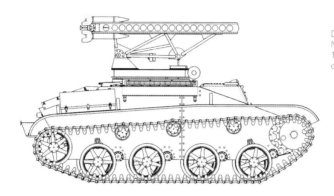

Drawings of the M-8 as built from November 1941 to the spring of 1942 on the GAZ produced T-60 chassis.

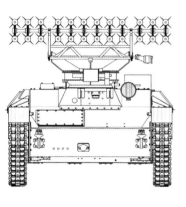
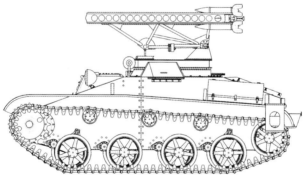

M-8 MRS on the T-60 chassis in transport configuration, with tarpaulins over the rocket launcher frames.

This BM-8 would appear to have been destroyed by its crew before capture. This (originally Wehrmacht) photograph was used in modified form in the Soviet illustrations also shown here, reflecting the lack of original photographs even available to the Soviet State.

An M-8 MRS destroyed in combat. (Tank Museum 2970/C5)

A rare service photograph of the BM-8 MRS. This particular vehicle was built on a GAZ chassis. Note the demonstration of a field repair (the disengaged wheels appear neither damaged nor missing). The rear idler is of the type manufactured at Plant №264.

A BM-8 destroyed in the summer of 1942. This vehicle was built on a Plant №38 chassis. Note the spoked and rubber rimmed road wheels and idler compared with the other BM-8 MRS vehicles pictured.

This BM-8, rebuilt to the original specifications, is located at the Museum of Military Glory of the Urals, Verkhnaya Pyshma, near Ekaterinburg. (Preserved Panzers)

Universal Artillery Platform

The idea of using the T-60 chassis to mount self-propelled artillery was first muted in November 1941, concurrent with the decision to cease production of the majority of tractors and artillery tractors in the Soviet Union, leaving the Red Army with no specialized artillery tow vehicles.

One potential solution to the problem was to develop self-propelled artillery systems based on series production tanks. The diminutive T-60 was not originally considered because the small size of the tank limited its development potential. A lengthened T-60 chassis could however accommodate a "regimental assault weapon" armed with a 76.2mm UVS or ZiS-3 dual-purpose gun, and the chassis could also be used for 25mm or 37mm self-propelled anti-aircraft mountings (known in Russian as ZSU).

A whole series of such self-propelled weapons, including several based on the T-60, were included in 1942 production plans according to documents dated November 1941. Development of self-propelled weapons on the T-60 chassis was assigned to S. A. Ginzburg, and on 29th January 1942, a design project was proposed with the TTTs for a preliminary universal self-propelled chassis design on the basis of T-60 components, with several variants as detailed below:

A. *Assault Gun for Support of Mechanized Troops*

1. *Intended for combined action with mechanized troops against tanks, bunkers, fortified points in settlements, as well as against enemy troops (firing shrapnel).*
2. *Vehicle weight in travelling order 7.5-8 tonnes, special trailers 3.5 - 4 tonnes.*
3. *System is to provide protection from small arms ammunition and HE shrapnel over the frontal aspects and in part the sides. The crew, engine, fuel tanks and ammunition complement are to be similarly protected to the T-60.*
4. *Ammunition complement not less than 20 rounds of fixed ammunition.*
5. *The system shall have a minimum horizontal arc of +/- 7° (preferably more), elevation from -5 to +30°.*
6. *The system design should ensure the capability of firing without trail spades.*
7. *Crew (including driver) 4-5.*

B. *Self-Propelled 37 mm Anti-aircraft Gun M-1939*

1. *Self-propelled gun (SAU) is intended to provide air-defence within motorized units, and also perform as anti-tank artillery.*
2. *The SAU system must be installed on an existing self-propelled chassis.*

3. *Weight of SAU in the travelling position - 7.0 tonnes.*
4. *The installation of the system on the chassis shall provide minimum firing height, and 360° traverse.*
a) *Maximum possible gun elevation and depression.*
b) *When firing from any position all fire calculations must be made on the platform.*
5. *Ammunition complement must be at least 150 rounds including armour-piercing and HE-Frag rounds.*
6. *Armour should be bulletproof semi-open type. Full armour of all basic components and the driver-mechanic's cab. No overhead armour.*
7. *Crew (including driver) - 7*

C. *Tank with turret installed 37 mm anti-aircraft gun of the Savin group type.*

1. *Self-propelled chassis, with turret installed 37mm anti-aircraft gun should be an anti-aircraft vehicle for mechanized forces based on a slightly heavier tank, while retaining the properties of a conventional tank against ground targets.*
2. *Turret installation must ensure full-circle fire horizontally and the angles of elevation from -5° to +85° and must have a special optical sight for anti-aircraft fire.*
3. *Hydraulic control mechanism must operate instantly.*
4. *The guns should be installed in a mantlet, coupled with a DT machine gun.*
5. *Ammunition at least 150 rounds of ammunition for 37 mm guns and at least 1500-2000 rounds for machine gun.*
6. *Armour should be in several variants as described above.*
7. *Tank weight: 8-10 tonnes.*
8. *Tank crew: 3-4.*

The NII-48 institute design for a turretless tank (SAU) version of the T-60 envisaged a vehicle armed with a 45mm tank gun and co-axial 7.62mm DT machine gun, with a secondary 7.62mm DT machine gun mounted in the driver-mechanic's sponson or "rubka". The NII-48 "turretless tank" project was presented for consideration in April 1942. (TsAMO)

D. *Light tank with armour to 45 mm, 45 mm gun and co-axial machine guns in the turret*

1. *A relatively lightweight chassis with dual engines creating the possibility of a light tank, better armed and armoured than the T-60. In the case of arrangement of two engines in the hull front, sufficient space is made available in the rear part of the vehicle for placement of a relatively powerful weapons platform.*
2. *A 45 mm gun and co-axial DT machine gun (preferably two) should be mounted in a single gun mantlet.*
3. *The armour of the tank can be determined in several ways as referred to above.*
4. *Tank weight: 9-10 tonnes.*
5. *Crew: 3-4.*

In addition to ZSU and assault SAU vehicle variants, the project thereby also included a tank design that could potentially replace the T-60, an alternative for the T-60 armed with the 37mm ZiS-19 tank gun and the new GAZ developed T-70. The superiority of the new GAZ developed T-70 design was however already clear by February 1942, and the series production launch of Astrov's T-70 was only a matter of time. Thus, when the GAU Artillery Committee (ArtKom) GAU KA met to review dedicated self-propelled artillery on 15th April 1942, they proposed that all future discussion of T-60 based SAUs be curtailed, and that all efforts be dedicated to work related to the T-70 chassis.

The T-60 chassis was not so easily killed off however. Development responsibility for light self-propelled guns was assigned to Plant №37, which just three days before the ArtKom meeting had been given a three month reprieve in its preparation for series production of T-70. Though Plant №37 plant management was not overly excited with the potential requirement to produce a SAU based on the chassis of the obsolescent T-60 tank, the plant was also nowhere near ready to series produce the new T-70, never mind SAUs on its chassis. Ginzberg and his design team remained interested in developing a universal light SAU chassis and consequently despite the obsolescence of the chassis two new T-60 chassis based SAU projects appeared in late April.

These original drawings of the NII-48 turretless tank project show the general configuration, armament, armour layout and of the miniature SAU self-propelled gun. The project envisaged using the engine, transmission and running gear of the T-60 The 45mm main armament is ball mounted together with the co-axial armament. The driver-mechanic and commander/loader/gunner sit alongside each other in the front of the vehicle, with the rear mounted engine driving the tracks via front mounted drive sprockets. (TsAMO)

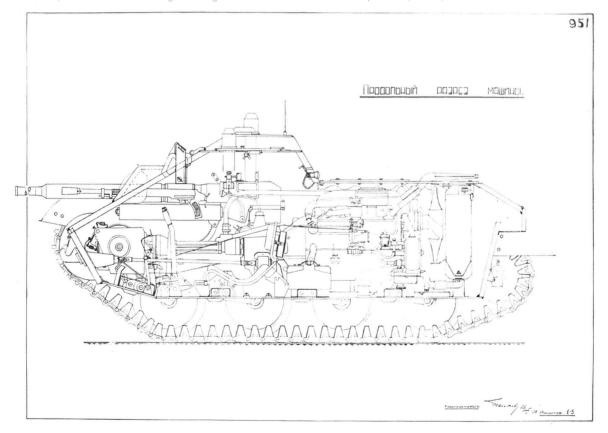

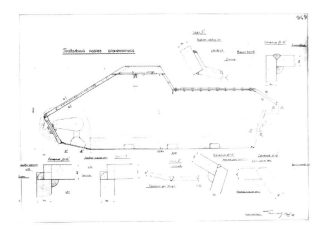
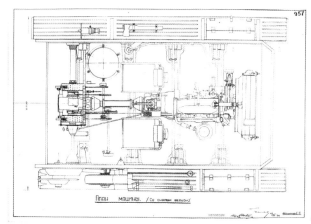
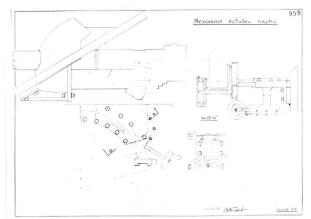
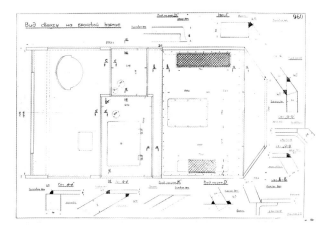

Layout and armour drawings for the NII-48 Institute SAU project, which envisaged a 45 mm tank gun as main armament. (TsAMO)

Obiekt-31 Universal Chassis

The first project, designated "Obiekt-31" (Object-31) or "Chassis 31", was a universal chassis designed to maximize the use of T-60 components. Development oversight was assigned to Department № 030 headed by design engineer K. E. Istomin. The "Obiekt-31" largely conformed to the technical requirements (TTTs) of the universal chassis proposed in January of 1942. The vehicle was based on the T-60 but with an elongated and widened chassis, with the number of road wheels on each side increased from 4 to 6, and the torsion bars lengthened from 1718 to 2225 mm in accordance with the increased vehicle width. Parallel mounted GAZ-202 engines provided the power, with the cooling system, transmission and final drive mechanism taken from the T-60. If required the vehicle could operate on a single engine, with an elongated control rod disconnecting the damaged engine by means of a transfer box.

There were three versions of the "Chassis 31" project, provided for installation of 25mm M-1940 (72-K) or 37mm M-1939 (61-K) anti-aircraft weapons, and as an alternative installation the 76mm M-1942 (ZiS-3) gun. A single 7.62mm DT machine gun provided defensive fire on all variants. The anti-aircraft variants had a 10mm armour basis, with the SAU version having 30mm armour over the frontal aspects and 10mm on the ides and rear. The 25mm ZSU was designated BGS-1, the 37mm ZSU designated BGS-2 and the SAU the BGS-3, with estimated combat weights of 9500kg, 9700kg and 9900kg, respectively.

Officially the theme of light SAU development was passed to Plant №38; however in early August 1942, the KB of Plant №8 presented the draft of a project for a 25-mm ZSU gun on the chassis of the SU-31, which received the index ZiK-5. This was followed by a draft project for an SAU on the base of the SU-32, which received the index ZiK-7-II, differing only in the casemate design and the installation of a 76-mm ZiS-5 gun (as in the BGS-5). Both projects were terminated.

Obiekt-32 Universal Chassis

The second project, designated "Obiekt-32" (Object-32) or "Chassis 32" was a universal chassis designed on the basis of T-70 components. Development was supervised by the design engineer N. N. Efimov at Department №030. The project envisaged use of the T-70 chassis, powered by the new GAZ-203 engine, with the gearbox, cooling system and final drives also taken with the T-70. As the T-70 was at the time not yet in production, the T-60 chassis with lengthened torsion bars was to be used for the prototype.

Unlike "Chassis 31", the primary intent of the "Obiekt-32" was to mount the 76mm ZiS-5 tank gun in an SAU chassis. A ZSU variant armed with either the 25 mm M-1940 (72-K) or 37mm M-1939 (61-K) anti-aircraft gun was envisaged as a secondary priority. As with the "Obiekt-31" all variants were to be armed with a 7.62mm DT machine-gun for local defense. The envisaged frontal armour of the 76mm ZiS-5 armed SAU variant was 35mm.

The ZSU variant of the "Obiekt-32" received the index BGS-4, the SAU variant the index BGS-5, with combat weights estimated at 8700 and 10500kg, respectively.

The priority for development between the "Chassis-31 and Chassis-32" was given to the "Chassis 31", a prototype of which had by early June been completed in mild steel. "Chassis 31" (which later received the index SU-31) was built in the BGS-2 variant. In July, "Chassis-32" was completed in the BGS-5 variant, with a 15mm mild steel armour basis on the superstructure, and received the index SU-32. The SU-31 was reported as having performed well during trials, however the engines on the SU-32 overheated. By the time of the trials, Plant №37 had in the meantime been consolidated with Uralmash in order to

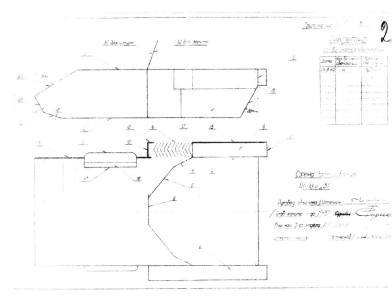

The armour scheme for the projected "Chassis-31", May 1942. (TsAMO)

concentrate on planned T-34 (chassis) production and the series production of a light SAU in the city of Sverdlovsk never progressed beyond the prototype testing stage.

T-133 Universal Chassis

Almost simultaneously with developments at Plant №37 a similar project was developed at NATI. The preliminary designs, designated T-133-B, T-133-V and T-133Zh were presented to the ArtKom GAU KA on 4th May 1942.

The ZiK-5 was a 25mm M-1940 anti-aircraft gun installation based on the SU-31 chassis. (TsAMO)

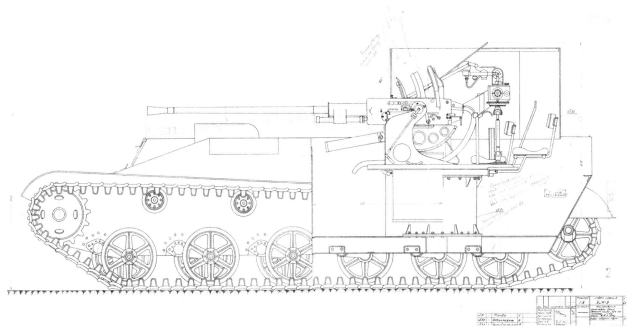

The SU-31 prototype outside Plant №37, summer 1942. The chassis has been widened and considerably elongated, with six road wheels on each side, spaced to distribute the vehicle and armament weight. The vehicle has a new open turret, giving limited protection to the crew of the 37mm anti-aircraft gun. The lightly armoured SU-31 had a high angle of fire, and could be used in the anti-aircraft and ground support roles. Note the three colour summer camouflage scheme. (TsAMO)

The T-133-B and T-133-V were 37mm ZSU anti-aircraft vehicles, while the T-133-Zh was armed with two 120mm mortars, with all variants having a combat weight of 7500 kg. All were to use parts from the T-60 and T-70 tanks. The T-133-B was to be powered by two GAZ-AA engines mounted in parallel, the T-133-V and T-133-Zh a ZiS-5 engine, installed at an angle. The T-133-V and T-133-Zh were not destined for further development, but the T-133-B was so approved. It was however now intended to use the T-133-B chassis as a base to create a 76mm SAU, ZSU variants with 25mm and 37mm anti-aircraft guns, and SAU with paired 120-mm mortars. As before, the 76mm SAU was the development priority. The prototypes were to be ready by August 1942, but they were never completed.

The last attempt to organize the production of SAUs based on the T-60 was made in September 1942. On 7th September, GABTU received a the memo from the designer engineers Surenyan and Efimov, who by that time had returned to Moscow from Sverdlovsk and were located back at the original site of Plant №37 prior to the evacuation of its machine tooling and engineers to safety beyond the Ural mountains. The letter in part stated that:

"Despite the numerical superiority of their tanks, the German army is working on the modernization and modification of tanks with weak armour and armament as tracked chassis for a variety of artillery systems. We have not reviewed this question sufficiently not only because of lack of direction in this area of design thought, but mainly because departmental relationships between GAU and GABTU KA. Questions about utilizing the obsolescent inventory with weak armour and armament as tracked SAUs must at present be of considerably more interest than their use as tanks. Working on the development of SAUs on the chassis of the T-60, T-70, SU-31, SU-32, only recently, and after building prototypes of these vehicles, we managed to find another solution, which gave an opportunity to use T-60 chassis as SAUs with limited rework of the hulls.

Because the T-60 is now out of production, this project can be used to rework previously released tanks, returned to repair plants, often with destroyed turret and armour, not required but for the transition to SAU use. As the T-60 was produced in large numbers, we consider it appropriate for their alteration of SAUs, representing much more interest than the T-60.

The following systems can be installed on the chassis of the T-60 tank:

1. *37mm anti-aircraft gun*
2. *25mm anti-aircraft gun*
3. *76mm gun ZiS-3 (divisional infantry gun)*
4. *57mm anti-tank gun ZiS-2*

The SU-31 was a precursor to the post-war ZSU-37 self-propelled anti-aircraft system, which was manufactured in small quantities immediately after the end of World War Two. These ZSU-37 vehicles are parading through Moscow's Red Square on 7th November 1946. (photographer - Sitnikov)

The OSU-76 was an early prototype airborne self-propelled gun developed specifically for the airborne forces. It used a reversed T-60 chassis and mechanical components. It was developed in the winter and spring of 1943-44. The concept would ultimately be developed into the post-war ASU-57 airborne self-propelled gun. (Kubinka archives)

The T-60 and later T-70 and their component parts were used to develop a variety of light self-propelled guns, such as the SU-57B. (Kubinka archives)

SAU versions of all of these systems should be of particular interest to the Red Army. At the present time ZSU anti-aircraft self-propelled guns are of significantly greater interest, it is possible initially to build and test the prototype for this in the T-60. Please immediately issue an instruction about the assembly of prototypes. This suggestion does not countermand the test samples of the SU-31 and SU-32, designed for new production. Management of all work can be delegated to N. N. Efimov. We believe that the proposal currently has a particular interest and ask You to take all possible measures to accelerate the implementation of this proposal, and to report our proposal to the Commissars comrade Fedorenko and comrade Molotov."

The proposal was considered, but further development was not undertaken on the already obsolescent T-60 chassis, although alternative designs continued to be proposed for a year. The T-60 was however rebuilt as a light SPG by Axis forces using captured T-60 chassis. The Romanian Army developed a light SAU, which consisted of mounting captured Soviet 76.2mm M-1936 (F-22) divisional guns on a lightly armoured open mounting installed on the T-60 chassis. The first examples of the Romanian built "Tun Anticar pe Afet Mobil T-60" (also known as the TACAM) were paraded in Bucharest on 10th May 1943, with 34 examples being built, which were recovered by the Red Army in 1944 when Romania changed

allegiance in the war. Romania also developed a fully enclosed SAU on the T-60 chassis, mounting a 152mm howitzer.

OSU-76 (OSA-76) Airborne Self-Propelled Gun

The OSU-76 (Obshevoiskovaya Samokhodnaya Ustanovka - General Purpose (all arms) -76mm calibre) light 76.2mm self-propelled gun was developed at Plant №38 using T-60 components in the spring and early summer of 1944. The vehicle was also known as the OSA-76 (Oblegchennaya Samokhodnaya Artustanovka - Lightweight Self Propelled Gun - 76mm calibre).

The OSU-76 initiative was a low cost, lightly armoured vehicle suitable for both ground and airborne forces use, becoming the first of a series of light airborne self-propelled guns that entered service with Soviet VDV airborne forces in the immediate post-war years. Components taken from the T-60 included (modified) final drives, road wheels, torsion bars, balancers and the track, with the armament being the 76.2mm M-1942 (ZiS-3) divisional gun. The 4.2 metric tonne combat weight vehicle was powered by a 4 cylinder GAZ-M engine developing 52hp. The OSU-76 represents a first link between the wartime T-60 and later T-70 and a range of light SAU prototypes that ultimately resulted in the series production post-war ASU-57 airborne (VDV) forces self propelled gun.

Air Defence Variants

In addition to creating a universal chassis, significant development work was undertaken in 1942-43 on the creation of dedicated air defence vehicles based on the T-60 chassis that would not involve major rework of the chassis as considered above, with modification being limited to fitment of a modified turret.

The development of self-propelled anti-aircraft tanks using modified standard tank turrets had begun in 1940 under the direction of the engineer I. V. Savin. His team developed an anti-aircraft turret for the T-50 to prototype stage, but work on this was curtailed due to the evacuation of T-50 production to its new location at Plant №174 (Omsk) where all concentration was inevitably on the production of line tanks. In January 1942, with the T-50 removed from production, the anti-aircraft turret design was carried forward to the T-34, but this project was never realized in steel, and the idea of producing anti-aircraft turrets for mounting on standard line tanks was latterly applied to the T-60 tank as production was re-established at Plant №37 in Sverdlovsk.

Meanwhile feedback from the front line during the first months of the war indicated that (towed) anti-aircraft guns attached to tank brigades had limited mobility and thereby could not provide effective cover on rough terrain. The development of self-propelled anti-aircraft turret installations therefore re-

started in August 1942, when, according to a memorandum from the chief engineer of Plant №37 N. N. Kozyrev *"the Deputy People's Commissar of Tank Industry (NKTP), comrade Zh. Ya Kotin has instructed (the plant to) in a very short time perform experimental work on the installation of DShK anti-aircraft machine guns in the turrets of the T-60 and T-70".*

The TTTs for developing a paired 12.7mm DShK installation for both the T-60 and T-70 were developed by 16th August 1942 under the heading *"To create a paired 12.7mm anti-aircraft "DShK" installation for the defense of mechanized columns from enemy air attack".* The TTTs defined that the weapons should be fitted in a standard T-60 turret, with the frontal aspects modified for the new installation within an open turret, and with new 42 round ammunition magazines.

Development work on anti-aircraft vehicle versions of the T-60 and T-70 at Plant №37 was controlled by Savin, who was at that time head of the group anti-aircraft self-propelled vehicles at OGK NKTP. Meantime GAZ was working concurrently on an anti-aircraft tank based on the new T-70 with plant records confirming that the prototype was completed by the beginning of September.

On 16th September 1942 GABTU and GAU KA issued Order №0107ss, according to which a Commission was established under the chairmanship of Engineer-Colonel Nenaro-

The SZU during polygon testing, July 1942. (TsAMO)

Overhead view of the cramped turret arrangement on the SZU. (TsAMO)

Side view of the SZU in ground support and anti-aircraft positions. (TsAMO)

SZU at maximum fire angle, with turret covers open. (TsAMO)

kov, and composed of Engineer-Colonel Rumyantsev and engineer-captain Vasilevsky (GABTU KA), engineer-captain Chemen (AK GAU), Astrov (NKSM), Savin (NKTP) and Maklakov representing GAZ.

The task of the Commission was to develop and test in the shortest possible time samples of anti-aircraft self-propelled gun installations. Prototypes of the light anti-aircraft tanks were presented for testing by the beginning of December 1942.

The T-60 and T-70 "Zenitniy" (anti-aircraft) tanks deve-

loped at Plant №37, were developed by Savin based on experience gained on previous projects, using series production tank turrets with minimal alterations, the turret front section being modified and the roof removed. The GAZ alternative, designated T-90, was based on the T-70 and fitted with a turret with a 35mm armour basis. All the turrets were open, with the T-60Z and T-90 being fitted with a collapsible awning for weather protection.

All three ZSU vehicles used a tandem 12.7mm DShKT

SZU rear view, with 12.7mm DShK armament at maximum elevation and turret covers open. Note the exhaust system with lagging and silencer. (TsAMO)

machine gun, with a return to the DK concept of the 1930s using a 30 round drum magazine. All used the K-8T sight for air-defence and the TMFP for use against ground targets. The sights were however mounted to the left of the guns on the T-90 and in the centre of the turret above the guns on the T-70Z.

Testing of the light ZSU vehicles began on 5th December 1942. The T-60 chassis used for the T-60 "Zenitniy" (also known as the T-60-3 or "063") was the very same chassis that had been used to test the ZiS-16 engine, which failed immediately before the trial, such that the T-60 "Zenitniy" arrived for trials without a running engine. The location of the sighting was immediately reviewed as inadequate, while operating the guns in the ground role proved near impossible due to the proximity of the turret ring. The Plant №37 developed T-60 "Zenitniy" was thereby dismissed from further testing, as was the Plant №37 developed T-70 "Zenitniy", which failed trials due to a number of structural defects, which Savin contested. The testing commission consequently recommended the T-90 for acceptance in the Red Army and service with ABT units (air defence battalions of tank units) after the remedy of some defects found during trials.

Savin, disagreeing with the final conclusions of the Commission wrote a lengthy list of comments, which was attached to the report. A few items from Savin's noted "special observations" shed light on the test procedures and some conclusions:

"The T-70 was fired from the left gun only at a distance of 100 m, firing 45 rounds of ammunition, and at a distance of 400 m - 20 rounds, clearly inadequate to determine a result. The right gun for the same reasons that are noted by the Board for the GAU KA for all units with machine guns DShK had some failures while firing on 6th July, and on 8th July the guns on the T-90 also worked intermittently. The specific causes of failure in the firing of all guns (T-70 and T-90) the Commission has not concluded on the test polygon, but it may relate to lubrication"

Savin went on to note that, in his opinion, the T-70 Zenitniy installation was a simple and inexpensive solution which could be built at repair plants without special equipment, such as the former Plant №37 in its original location. By contrast he was of the opinion that the new cast turret components for the T-90 "Zenitniy" required plants such as GAZ and Plant №38 etc. with better equipment levels to complete. Further, though the T-70 "Zenitniy" turret could be retrofitted to the T-60,

SZU, with armament in anti-aircraft position and turret hatch covers closed. (TsAMO)

T-60 "Zenitniy" (T-60-3) developed by the Savin design group during trials at the end of 1942. The vehicle was also known as the T-60-3. (TsAMO)

the T-90 "Zenitniy" turret would require major modifications to the T-60 design, not least to the turret race. Regarding the T-60 "Zenitniy" which had been dropped before testing began, Savin suggested changing the mantlet to that of the T-70 "Zenitniy", with the guns and collimator sight moved forward by 150 mm to provide better clearance with the turret ring in the ground fire role would resolve the problems encountered.

Savin also advised that after the official trials some additional non-official tests had been conducted against a flying kite which showed the T-60 "Zenitniy" in a much more favourable light. Despite his ongoing efforts, Savin's opinions were largely ignored, as the T-90Z turret installation was developed for the next-generation T-70 then in series production at two plants, whereas the T-60 was almost 6 months out of production.

Meanwhile, on 15th December 1942, the People's Commissar of Medium Machine Building (NKSM), Akopov, was sent a draft GKO resolution, which proposed launching series production of not only the T-90, but also the discredited T-60-Z (as it was referred to in GABTU correspondence):

"1. To adopt the Armoured and Mechanized forces of the Red Army - tandem 12.7mm anti-aircraft "DShKT" machine guns mounted in the turret of the T-70, designed and manufactured by the Gorky "Molotov" Automotive Plant.

2. To oblige NKTP (comrade Saltsmann) and the Director

of Plant №37 (comrade Zelikson) to by 1st February 1943 prepare the production of tanks re-armed with a tandem anti-aircraft mounting and to start production of repaired and rebuilt T-60 tanks using the drawings approved by GABTU KA.

3. To oblige NKV (comrade Ustinov) and NKO (GAU KA) to manufacture and supply Plant №37 with:

a) 12.7 mm machine guns, "DShKT"

b) 12.7mm "DShKT" machine gun magazines with a capacity of 42 rounds.

b) Collimator sights.

g) Optical sights "TMFP".

4. To oblige NKSM (comrade Akopov) and the Director of the Gorky "Molotov" Automobile Plant (comrade Livshits) to by 1.1.43 develop drawings for the installation of the turret with anti-aircraft mounting (designed by the Gorky Automobile Plant) on the T-60, outfit the tank and by 5.1.43 to submit to GABTU KA and NKTP for approval."

Throughout the winter of 1943 preparation work was carried out for the production of anti-aircraft tanks mounted on both the T-70 and the by now obsolete T-60 chassis. Work on the implementation of the T-90 was meantime delayed, and in the meanwhile series production of the T-90 was now planned to be undertaken at Plant №40, using the chassis of the up-armoured T-80 light tank.

In the spring of 1943, GAZ returned to the idea of a self-propelled anti-aircraft installation based on the T-60 as originally considered in September 1942, to be built on the chassis of T-60 tanks returned for repair. The new prototype, completed in July 1943 and designated SZU (self-propelled anti-aircraft gun) by the plant, used a T-60 tank built in March-April 1942 with an "ekranirovanny" shielded hull.

Savin's words about the "ease" of installation of the T-90 turret on the T-60 turret race proved prophetic. GAZ had to build the turret for the new SZU prototype practically from scratch, with a shape completely different from that used on the T-60 and T-70. The design took into account comments not only on the T-90, but also a 37mm Sh-37 (ZUT) anti-aircraft turret installation developed at OKB-15.

As in the case of ZUT, the turret roof of the SZU was almost completely closed by hinged panels, there is a small turret bustle which housed the 12-R radio station. The tandem 12.7mm DShKT machine gun installation was taken complete with mantlet from the T-90, but some elements, particularly the location of the collimator sight was changed. The firing of the guns was carried out using an electrical solenoid, provided bursts and single shot operation. The speed of aiming in both horizontal and vertical planes were brought up to 10° for one turn of the flywheel. The total combat weight of the SZU was 6,420 kg, comparable to the series production T-60.

The SZU prototype was tested from 12th to 25th July 1943, with firing trials and 200km of mobility trials on roads and rough terrain to test the stability of the alignment of the sights. As with the T-90, firing trials were not conducted using a cone towed behind an aircraft as was normal test procedure. The trials results noted an imbalance of the T-60 turret race, and the not entirely successful design of folding roof panels (with the panels closed there was insufficient headroom).

Test firing against ground targets showed good accuracy, though accuracy while travelling was reduced sharply (from 60 rounds fired, 42 hit the target on seven attempts fired at a range of 400 metres). The 70° maximum elevation was considered insufficient, with an elevation of 85° being recommended, albeit during trials there had been delays when firing at angles of elevation greater than 40°, as well as jamming of the cartridges requiring redesign of the ejection ports. It was recommended that the TMFP sights be replaced with the shorter 5T type, and to drastically increase the ammunition complement from 480 to 1500 rounds. The trial conclusion per Soviet norms listed the deficiencies that required modification, but there was not a word about any prospect of serial production.

As in the case of similar anti-aircraft tank variants developed on the chassis of T-70 and T-80, the SZU (also known as the "063" or T-60-3) did not progress beyond the prototype stage. The anti-aircraft versions of the T-60 that were un-dis-

T-60 "Zenitniy" (T-60-3), side view. (TsAMO)

putably required at the front were hindered in that the number of damaged T-60 hulls which could be retuned from the front for modification was not guaranteed, while the 12.7mm DK machine gun with its drum magazine was not at the time in series production. A T-95 "Zenitniy" tank was apparently also developed on paper but did not progress further.

The development of light anti-aircraft gun mountings on small and light tank chassis was ultimately a development "tupik" (a dead-end) during the war years. Several variants were developed by a number of plants and design bureaus, and several prototypes built and tested, but none entered service with the Red Army. During the war years, mechanized anti-aircraft cover was provided by vehicles such as the GAZ and ZiS trucks mounting the "4M" quadruple 7.62mm PM-1910 "Maxim" anti-aircraft machine gun, and vehicles such as the US M5 half-track based M17 MGMC as provided to the Soviet Union under Lend-Lease. The first purpose designed (limited) series production anti-aircraft vehicle, the ZSU-37 (based on a modified SU-76 chassis), would not appear in service until immediately after the end of the war.

KT Flying Tank

Perhaps the most technically challenging, unique and fair to say bizarre variant of the T-60 was the KT (A-40) flying tank, which despite appearing an entirely improbable development concept actually took to the skies, albeit briefly.

The idea of transporting tanks by air was first mooted in the early 1930s, with one of the main protagonists of this concept being the American engineer John Walter Christie. Christie struggled to have his designs accepted for series production in his native country; however the Soviet Union took a particular interest in his work. Christie's original M-1931 wheel/track tank design was sold to the Soviet Union where it was ultimately developed into the BT fast tank series. Christie had also considered the concept of a towed glider mounted tank and, with the advent of more powerful aircraft with heavier payload lift capacity, also considered the concept of an airborne tank being suspended under aircraft wings and airlifted to its intended destination. Neither concept was ultimately pursued in the United States; however both Christie's flying tank concept and that of airlifting armoured vehicles suspended under heavy transport aircraft wings were developed to fruition in the Soviet Union.

This tank-glider concept was proposed by the aviation engineers Ermonsky, Solovyov and Matsuk at the TsAGI aircraft design institute in June 1941. The design envisaged the mounting of a tail section and wings to a 6 metric tonne light tank, to be towed aloft by a heavy transport aircraft. The drawing is dated 20th June 1941, two days before the outbeak of war on the Eastern Front. Though not developed to prototype stage, the theme was revisited a year later with the development of the KT glider tank. (TsAMO)

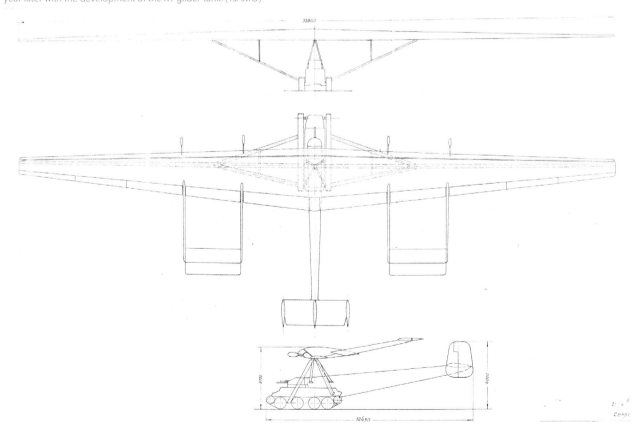

For flight trials, the turret of the T-60 tank was removed from the KT (A-40) tank glider to reduce take-off weight and improve airflow, hence towed take-off speed. (RGAE)

From the mid 1930s, the Soviet Union began to experiment with the suspension of personnel, vehicles and latterly even small tanks mounted under the wings of the TB-3 heavy bomber on special suspension mountings, of which a total of 130 sets were built to mount the T-37A and T-38 amphibious reconnaissance tanks. Experiments were even conducted whereby T-37A tanks were dropped directly into water; however the landing ruptured the hull in all cases with the tanks subsequently sinking.

On 22nd February 1941, NKO Resolution №23ss was issued which required the People's Commissariat of Heavy Engineering (NKTM) to manufacture a batch of 12 suspension units with a capacity of 5.5 metric tonnes for the new TB-7 (PE-8) bomber. These suspension units were intended to mount the T-40, with 11 T-40 tanks being sent to the 205th Airborne Desant Battalion located at Borispol in Ukraine (today Kiev international airport) in March 1941 for trials.

Meantime, and perhaps even more radical at the time than mounting tanks under heavy bombers was the development of tank gliders, with several design groups within TsAGI (the Central Aero Hydrodynamic Institute) working on separate tank glider designs. Several designs, such as that developed by the aircraft designer A. Ya. Shcherbakov initially offered designs capable of transporting tankettes specially developed for airborne applications at NATI, with a combat weight of 3-6

metric tonnes. The Soviet Union was embroiled in total war before the designs had a chance to mature, with the pre-war priority of giving the T-40 airborne capability being replaced by the need to give the T-60 that same capability by the autumn of 1941. Development continued, albeit with other more pressing priorities, during the months after Operation "Barbarossa".

According to a letter from the acting chief of the 11th Main Directorate of the People's Commissariat of Aviation Industry (NKAP) Pavel Vladimirovich Tsybin dated 21st August 1941, a heavy transport glider with a load capacity of 1850kg was expected to be submitted for trials in September, however there is no subsequent information on the ultimate fate of this glider design.

In December 1941 the theme of a "desant T-60" glider was submitted by the aircraft designer Oleg Konstantinovich Antonov, who is today synonymous with Russian heavy transport aircraft and at the time held the position of chief engineer of the Glider Command (PU) of NKAP.

At the end of 1941, in response to the NKAP requirement for such a tank desant system the O.K. Antonov design bureau offered the design of a "Krilaty Tank" or "Krilya Tanka" (literally "tank with wings" or "winged tank", abbreviated to KT), also known by the designation A-40. The design envisaged that the "KT" be towed aloft by a heavy transport aircraft. It would then be released 20-25km from its intended landing zone, and would subsequently descend in silence to gain the element of surprise. On landing, the pilot, who also acted as tank driver/mechanic, would release the wings mechanically from within the tank by means of a special release lever, and then move off to engage enemy formations as a conventional tank, with the second member of the crew (the commander/gunner/loader) operating the armament. The aircraft selected for trials was the four-engine TB-3 heavy bomber, and the tank chosen was the T-60, with GAZ in December being requested to supply a standard production tank for trials.

The KT consisted of a T-60 tank to which a biplane glider assembly with twin tail booms and twin tail rudders was mounted, attached directly to the tank at four points. As the glider was intended for single time disposable use Antonov planned to produce the glider from the cheapest available materials.

The glider prototype was manufactured at an aviation (glider) plant in Tyumen in April 1942, to where Antonov's Moscow region based KB had been evacuated in the autumn of 1941. The KT glider (also known as the A-T, the AT-1 and as the A-40) had a total fusclage length of 12 metres, and an 18 metre wingspan with a total surface area of 86m2. The decision to use a biplane design with steel bracing cables was made in

order to maximize the wing surface area - and hence lift - while minimizing the overall wingspan that a single wing design would have required. The glider had a total take-off weight of 7.3 metric tonnes (7.8 according to some sources) and a glider weight of 2.0 metric tonnes. The tank had a weight of 5.8 metric tonnes, with the discrepancy likely being due to the removal of the turret for trials.

In the summer of 1942, the tank and airframe combination was delivered to the LII test institute of the Red Army Air Force (VVS) at Stakhanovo (today Zhukovsky) in the southern suburbs of Moscow. Testing began on 7th August 1942 with the turret having been removed to reduce takeoff weight. Three high-speed taxi-runs were undertaken on the runway at 110-115 km/h to test the ability of the T-60s running gear. Perhaps surprisingly considering the T-60 had a normal maximum speed of 45km/h, the acceleration tests were successful and the running gear proved capable of absorbing the stresses involved. There followed a test "flight" where the KT was lifted aloft to approximately 4m above the ground for a short duration on the runway in order to test the glider's control surfaces.

The first full test flight was scheduled for 2nd September 1942. As no TB-7 (Pe-8) bombers were available for the test, an older TB-3 bomber with the four AM-34RN engines uprated to 970hp was used for the flying trials. The TB-3 was piloted by test pilot Pavel A. Eremeev, himself a former glider designer, with the KT glider tank piloted by test pilot Sergei Nikolaevich Anokhin. The first (and as it would turn out the last) flight of the KT glider tank was conducted on schedule on 2nd September 1942.

The highly improbable looking KT (A-40) glider, built around a T-60 tank, was not only built in the summer of 1942, but was actually towed aloft and flew, if briefly, during trials. The turretless T-60 based KT (A-40) "flying tank" glider prototype is shown parked at the edge of an airfield, summer 1942. (RGAE)

A model of the KT (A-40) as it would have appeared in flight in early 1942. (RGAE)

On takeoff it became clear that in view of the large aerodynamic drag of the tank glider the maximum airborne towing speed was 130 km/h, and the flight altitude did not exceed 40 metres. Eremeev attempted to increase the airborne towing speed to 140km/h but in consequence the aircraft engines began to overheat. It was clear that the test would require to be abandoned prematurely, and Eremeev made the decision to release the KT over the nearby Bykovo airfield, thereby allowing the KT to glide back to the ground. Meantime, sitting in the T-60 glider, Anokhin as a professional test pilot was able to land the KT at the airfield without difficulty. Having landed safely he then started the engine and drove the KT slowly towards the airfield command post with the wings still attached. He was thereupon intercepted and arrested by the airfield guards, who like the air defence units at Bykovo had not been informed of the trials taking place at the almost adjacent airfield; which as the base commander explained to him had nearly resulted in him being shot down. The air defence crews in particular had not been expecting to see flying tanks that (or any other) day. With honour satisfied all round, Anokhin was released, and

An artist's illustration of the KT tank glider with turret fitted.

A Russian drawing of the KT tank glider.
(A.P. Krasilshikov)

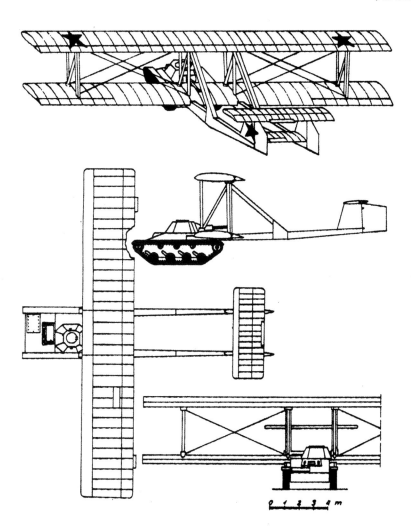

The TD-200 prototype clearing a wooden beam during test evaluation. The T-60 lineage is evident in this view.

Although the idea of tank trailers was being considered by several designers at the time, Chizhikov had made the conscious decision to propose his design to Plant №200, which adopted the design as their own, greatly increasing the likelihood of the "TD" being developed in metal. Besides, Chizhikov's design was simple, had a relatively low combat weight and used worn or scrap T-60 components in its construction so represented a good use for available materials.

A design group headed by senior designer Krasilnikov and plant KB chief Sergeyev, was set up at Plant №200 to consider the viability of the "TD" for series production, with Chizhikov acting as consultant. According to a report dated 20th March from the senior military representative of the Plant №200 military engineer 2nd rank Pestov, the plant had almost completed

Side view of the TD-200 armoured trailer №2, outside Plant №200, June 1942. (TsAMO)

three prototype armoured trailers, given the index TD-200 (Transport Desantniy - Plant №200). Pestov's report stated:

"Fabrication and testing of these three trailers will be completed by 20-22nd March, after which they will be sent to one of the departments in formation at the Kirov plant, as agreed with regional engineers.

On the first trailers the T-60 chassis and running gear has been used, because it was easiest to obtain and fastest to manufacture. In the future to reduce the cost of the trailer it will be necessary to use the chassis and running gear of old tractors, such as STZ-KhTZ.

Besides, it is necessary to consider the appropriateness of the armour thickness; whether simple firing ports or ball mounts are required; whether viewing devices are required; what the requirements for hatches are, etc.

For my part, I believe that these trailers are essential to the Red Army and after the first results of combat trials their full series production should be organized, furthermore for the armour can be used Kuznetsk and Magnitogorsk armoured plate with various defects and deviations found after chemical analysis. Therefore I will do everything possible to quickly manufacture, testing and dispatch these trailers to the front." (signed) military engineer 2nd rank Pestov - senior military representative of Plant №200.

The first prototypes had most of the characteristics originally proposed by Chizhikov. Troop embarkation and egress was via double hatches on the roof, in the forward section and the rear, with another emergency hatch located on the hull floor. According to GABTU requirements, the TD-200 was to allow troop egress through the rear at halt and on the move. The desant troops were seated on benches, with 5 on each. Grab handles (shortened from

---

*The S-2 (Skorostnoi – fast) was a heavy tracked tractor variant of the S-65 built in small numbers; however it bore Stalin's name, which may have been useful for the author of the letter in the circumstances.

the type used on the KV heavy tank) were mounted at the front and rear of the vehicle. There were a total of 10 firing ports with hinged covers, three on each side, 2 at the front and 2 at the rear.

TD-200 plant trials began on 16th April. The first trial run with TD-200 №1 towed behind a KV-1 heavy tank covered 48km, of which 37km was on cobbled roads and 11km on dirt roads, with an average speed of 16 km/h. The TD-200 twice lost its tracks during the trial while being manoeuvred over forward and reverse slopes, which was attributed to insufficient track tension. The 30cm ground clearance was declared insufficient; the trailer could not be decoupled from the KV-1 tow tank on the move, and the ability for the hatches to be opened from the outside while in service was considered unacceptable. After initial testing the single roof hatch design was reconfigured, delaying further trials by a month. Concerned by the fate of his project, Chizhikov wrote Stalin another letter on 22nd April with a request to assist acceleration of the work, without any result.

The second trials stage took place from 19th to 25th May, which coincided with military exercises conducted at the Chelyabinsk tank polygon; this time conducted over 28km of terrain with 20 desant troops within the vehicle. It took 60 seconds for all 20 desant troops to exit at halt, with the exercise successfully repeated with the tank and trailer combination moving at 4-5km/h. The fully loaded trailer overcame 1.2 metre deep holes in the ground. A 25cm diameter log was placed between the tracks of the tank and trailer, which was also overcome without difficulty. The trailer suffered some minor wheel and track damage while overcoming obstacles and the tow brace was bent out of shape but the TD-200 did not shed its tracks during the second trial.

Plant trials were completed on 15th June. Inspection of the chassis of TD-200 №1 showed all components to be within normal limits, and the trailer successfully passed the plant test program. Meantime the plant had built TD-200 prototypes №2 and №3, which were completed in early June as TD-200 №1 was undergoing trials.

The tests were successful; however for undefined reasons the TD-200 did not progress beyond trails stage - though the combat weight and the need for KV heavy tanks as tow vehicles was doubtless indicative.

The TD-200 program was never officially cancelled, but it does not feature further in wartime correspondence. A meeting convened on 27th February 1942, attended by commanders and deputies of the technical units of the 31st, 33rd, 62nd and 143rd tank brigades, at which the tactical and technical requirements (TTTs) for armoured sleds required by the Red Army were defined offers an explanation as to the cancellation of the TD-200 program. At the February meeting, the infantry complement for such armoured APC trailers was set at 15 desant troops, with a maximum trailer combat weight of 5 metric tonnes, which the 10 tonne TD-200 with its 20 man crew clearly exceeded on all counts, perhaps explaining its sudden demise. The reasoning might equally have been financial. The defined price in the contract between BTU KA and Plant №200 for producing the three armoured trailer prototypes was 126,000 rubles, or 42,000 rubles each. Considering that the trailers were to be built from scrap hulls, the price was excessive compared with the price for a T-60 line tank.

In addition to the TD-200, Plant №200 in May 1942 developed a chemical trailer, which received the index Gusenichniy Khimicheskiy Pritsep - tracked chemical trailer, abbreviated to GKhP, with a dual role of infecting and disinfecting areas, and also for laying smoke screens. The GKhP resembled the TD-

Rear view of the TD-200 armoured trailer №2, outside Plant №200, June 1942. (TsAMO)

Rear view of the TD-200 armoured trailer №2 with all desant infantry hatches open, Plant №200, June 1942. (TsAMO)

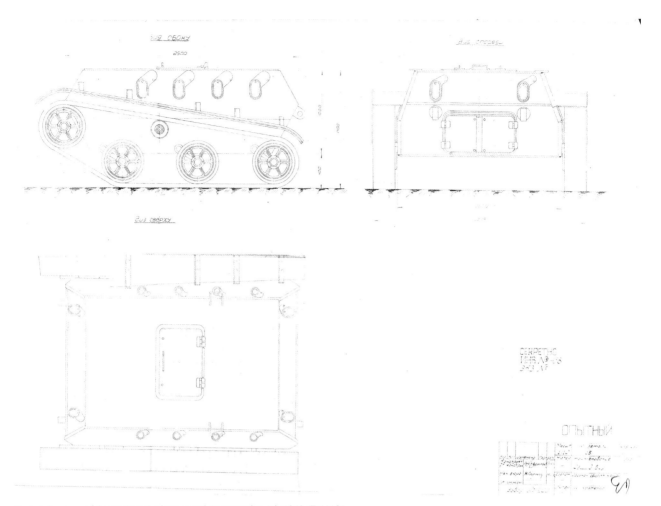

Project drawings of the TD-2 tracked armoured desant trailer, July 1942. (TsAMO)

200 in construction, but mounted a box construction on the tracked chassis within which were located reservoir tanks for toxic chemicals or a smoke generating mix. Gas was dispensed through a device located in the rear of the trailer. The GKhP trailer was offered in three versions, differing from each other by the internal layout and the internal volume of the tanks.

The GKhP chemical trailer project was reviewed by the 4th Department of GVKhU KA (the main military-chemical control of the Red Army) at the end of June 1942, with the conclusions reported on 3rd July:

"The KB of Plant №200 offers a tracked chemical trailer for the "KV" and "T-34" tanks. The GKhP is designed to contaminate ground, dispense gas, smoke and for ground decontamination.

The chemical equipment is mounted on a desant (APC) type trailer, developed and built by Plant №200 in the form of prototypes.

In consultation with BTU GABTU KA installed with the scarcity of trucks, with high quality steel for suspension and mounts for the tank.

The main direction for the design of tank trailers decided to go through the creating series production of tank trailer sleds,

with lower capacity chemical apparatus than can be obtained based on a tracked trailer, but the lack of scarce materials, parts and cheap to manufacture. Chemical trailer tow-suggests a broader tactical use than the GKhP"

The report concluded that in view of the scarcity of a number of materials and chassis components of the trailer the manufacture of prototypes would not be possible; however, somewhat in contradiction, that for accepting the TTTs for the trailer-sled one example would be built for development work. The GKhP was not further developed, perhaps for the same reason as the TD-200; however the development of armoured trailers at Chelyabinsk did not end there. Lieutenant-General Ya. Fedorenko, the chief of GABTU KA on 5th July 1942 received a letter from the chief engineer of Plant №200 L. I. Eiranov:

"Our plant has developed, apart from the tank trailer TD-200, another two variants of tank trailers: the TD-2 and TD-3 differing from the TD-200 in dimensions, weights and number of crew.

The TD-2 is designed for a crew of 15 when the armour thickness is: sloping side - 40 mm, front 30 mm, hull roof 15 mm, hull floor 10 mm, weight with full 1125kg payload is 5750kg, (or) with armour thickness: sloping side - 30 mm, front - 20 mm, hull roof -15 mm, hull floor - 10 mm, weight with full payload is 5100 kg.

TD-3 is designed for a crew of 20 when the armour thickness is: sloping side - 40 mm, front 30 mm, hull roof 15 mm, hull floor 10 mm, weight with full 1500kg payload is 7850 kg (or) with armour thickness: sloping side - 30 mm, front - 20 mm, hull roof - 15 mm, hull floor - 10 mm, weight with full payload is 7000 kg.

Submitted for your review are developed projects of the type TD-2 and TD-3, please allow us to manufacture a prototype of the TD-3."

After reviewing the letter Fedorenko made a hand written reply across the original letter in typical Soviet style, authorizing production of the TD-2 rather than the TD-3 as originally requested, as the characteristics of the TD-3 with its larger crew and greater combat weight also fell outside the TTTs for such armoured trailers approved 27th February 1942. The TD-2 was by contrast within the approved norms and was given the go-ahead.

According to a report by P.K. Voroshilov who was put in charge of the TD-2 project, the prototype was completed by 10th October and successfully completed plant trials. At the time the rival idea of building desant trailers on the base of tanks decommissioned from service was however considered more viable than building new vehicles from the same basic components. Surviving documentation indicates that three prototype TD-200 desant trailers as built in Chelaybinsk were at the end of September 1942 sent to the 19th Tank Brigade located on the Stalingrad front, which was at the time also being used to test tank mounted night vision devices.

On 11th September 1942 the TTTs for the design for "tank armoured sleds" were presented:

"Tank towed sleds intended to transport desant troops against enemy defences, and the delivery of these troops behind enemy lines".

The design requirements were specified as:

1. The height of the sled shall not exceed 650 mm.
2. Armour should protect a soldier from rifle and machine gun fire from any distance.
3. The sled must have armoured protection on all sides.
4. Hatches shall be located so as to provide quick release of the soldiers and so that under all conditions when leaving, the soldiers did not come under enemy fire.

Project drawings of the TD-3 tracked armoured desant trailer, July 1942. (TsAMO)

5. *For towing by tanks to develop a towing device that allows the sled to be uncoupled from within.*

6. *To provide hatches in front and sides for personal weapons fire.*

7. *The sled length and width to be as required for 16-20 people lying in prone position. The maximum width of the sled should not exceed the dimensions of the tank.*

8. *The bottom of the sled should have two channels to prevent sliding.*

9. *The sled must be reliable in service.*

10. *For the purpose of easy transport sleds long distances in trucks, it should quickly be assembled and dismantled.*

11. *Frontal armour should have such a form that snow does not build up there.*

These requirements were rejected for several reasons, not least of which was that placing 16-20 infantry within such a confined space was unworkable, while the trailer design specification was limited to 2500kg, and the width to 2200 mm. The proposed TTTs were however the catalyst for the creation of a new generation of armoured sleds, the most suitable donor

tank for which was the T-60 that had been removed from series production in July 1942. The available number of donor hulls and turrets was considerable. As of 11th November 1942, GAZ still retained some 212 T-60 hull and turret sets in storage, together with 47 hull and turret sets for the T-30, while 120 T-60 hulls and 50 turrets also remained in storage at Plant №37. With such volumes the idea of assembling "Bronepritsep" (BP) (armoured trailers) using T-60 hulls had considerable merit, as the hull and turrets sets were available in inventory, and production costs were minimal.

In September 1942, engineers at NATI had also addressed GABTU regarding the development of armoured sleds mounted on the T-60 chassis. The design drawings for the project, designated DP-60 (Desantniy Pritsep (DP) (desant trailer) were developed by the NATI engineers L. F. Kiselev and V. F. Goranov, and the following conclusion given:

"Presented, the conceptual design of a desant trailer(DP) in 3 versions intended to utilize existing T-60 hulls for the purpose of transporting, towed behind tanks, manpower and ammunition in

Project drawings of the GKhP tracked armoured chemical trailer, dated 20th May 1942. (TsAMO)

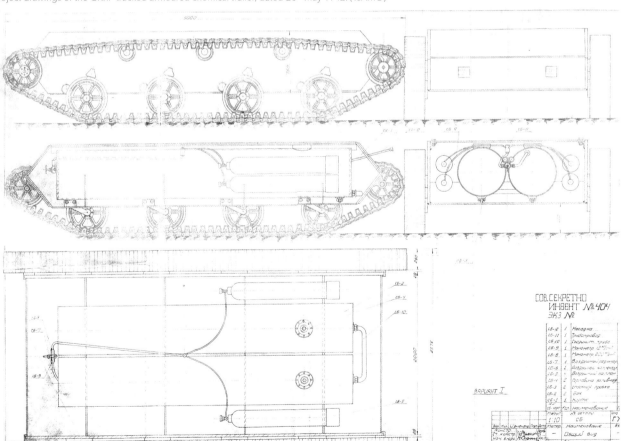

T-34 of Plant №112 production towing two GAZ built BP-60 armoured sleds, 13ᵗʰ January 1943 (TsAMO)

winter conditions. The most useful version of the trailer is with skis located under the hull floor and a turret".

There followed a list of modifications which included locating hatches in the hull rear armour, closing over all the holes left by removing the drive sprocket, roadwheel mounting stubs, torsion bars, idler wheel and return rollers, and the apertures left after the removal of the engine and associated cooling and exhaust arrangements. Firing ports were to be fitted in the hull side armour for use of personal weapons. All internal partitions were to be removed and seats installed to accommodate eight desant infantry. Skis were to be fitted to mountings welded to the hull floor. A special towing device was to be fitted

enabling the sled to be towed behind tanks, with a mechanical disconnect allowing the sled to be released from the tow tank from within the sled. The purposes to which the sled could be applied in winter conditions were listed as:

- Delivery of desant troops;
- Transport of ammunition and fuel;
- Removal of wounded from the battlefield;
- Use as a light armoured machine-gun nests;
- Assist engineers in the transportation of explosives;

The listed design features further included the option to mount turrets, armed with 7.62mm DT or DP Degtyarev machine guns, and to fit periscopes in the hull roof for obser-

Desant crew egress from the BP-60 armoured sled during trials, 13-14th January 1943.

the firing ports was considered entirely adequate, though it was noted that there were several visibility dead zones whereby the "bronesani" could be approached with impunity - albeit the T-34 located up front might dissuade any approach. It was however noted that while driving on powdery virgin snow on country roads the clouds of snow raised made it impossible for the desant troops to aim or use their personal weapons.

During the tests attempts at a turning radius of less than 20 metres resulted in the tubular tow drawbars deforming and the towing mount welds fracturing, forcing the trials to be abandoned.

Despite the shortcomings identified during the tests, the overall test conclusions were positive as indicated in the trial conclusions:

1. *The bronesani presented for test can transport 10 desant in-*
   fantry troops, and be used as armoured firing points at halt.
2. *A T-34 tank can simultaneously tow two bronesani.*
3. *The design of the tow mechanism allows the bronesani to*
   be decoupled on the move.

4. *The strength of the tow drawbar does not allow the brone-*
   sani to turn with a radius of less than 20 metres.
5. *Bronsani are recommended for adoption by the Red on the*
   proviso that the defects noted in the section "test results"
   are resolved.

Thus, the series production of "bronesani" was finally given the go-ahead, the production of "bronesani" using T-60 hulls beginning at both Plant №180 in Saratov and GAZ in Gorky in January 1943. In addition to producing "bronesani" on the basis of the T-60 hull, Plant №180 also completed a batch of 18 "bronesani" using spare T-50 hulls.

As of January 1943, with two full months of winter ahead, the T-60 based "bronesani" produced at Plant №180 and GAZ entered service with the Red Army. They were not however the first to enter service, as according to GABTU correspondence, units of the 65th Army had successfully used tanks towing field-built skid-mounted " bronesani" based on T-60 hulls which had originated from Plant №264 in the early winter of 1942-43.

BP-60 armoured sleds could be paired by means of a towbar connected between them, with a release cable above, which allowed the trailers to be disconnected from within the sleds. (TsAMO)

As of 3rd March 1943, GAZ had completed 250 "bronesani", 35 of which had been dispatched to the 1st Tank Army, 75 to the Western front and 41 to the North-Western front. Plant №180 in Saratov had meantime dispatched 24 "bronesani" to the Kalinin front. For obvious reasons the "bronesani" were not used during the summer months, but as of 21st December 1943 plant documents show that there were 120 completed "bronesani" held in storage at GAZ, which it was planned to deliver to several fronts for the coming winter warfare season - 60 to the 2nd Pribaltic front, 30 to the 1st Pribaltic front and 30 to the Belarusian Front. The exact number of BP-60 "bronesani" produced is unknown, but the combined total production output from GAZ and Plant №180 is approximately 300 armoured trailers, of which the majority were assembled at GAZ.

The BP-60 towbar was damaged when the armoured road train was subjected to tight turns during trials.

Chapter 7

T-60 Description and Walkarounds

The T-60 had a slightly unconventional layout, with the crew seated in tandem. The driver-mechanic was seated at the front of the tank, slightly to the left of the centerline, and was provided with a "rubka" or sponson due to the significantly low profile of the hull and steep glacis armour slope. The tank commander was located behind the driver-mechanic, performing the combined functions of commander, gunner and loader. Crew access was via a hatch immediately above the driver-mechanic's head, with the tank commander having access via the turret hatch.

The T-60 was armed with a 20mm TNSh (also sometimes referred to as the TNSh-1 or TNSh 20) automatic cannon, derived from the ShVAK weapon developed for use on Soviet ground attack and fighter aircraft, with a co-axial 7.62mm DT machine gun.

The 6 cylinder in-line GAZ-202 petrol engine was mounted on the right side off the tank, occupying the central and rear part of the hull. The 4 speed transmission was mounted ahead of the engine, driving the front-mounted drive sprockets via a single disc main clutch and side friction clutches controlled by linkages from the driver-mechanic's position. T-60 tanks could be fitted with conventional exhausts with the exhaust pipe running over the rear engine deck to a silencer on the rear armour plate, or fitted with a simplified fan-tail exhaust on the engine deck, without silencer.

T-60 hulls and turrets vary significantly, with 13-15mm base armour and variations in armour thickness depending on whether the tank had additional "ekranirovka" armour plating added to the base armour. The hull was assembled of RHA steel armour plate, with riveted and welded construction being used

Frontal view of a restored T-60 belonging to the Muzei Tekhniki (the Vadim Zadorozhny Museum) near Krasnogorsk, during a historical event at the State Technical Museum at Chernogolovka, 21st June 2014.

A side view of the same T-60 tank at Chernogolovke, 21st June 2014.

throughout, with riveting replaced by welding as production stabilized, and with myriad variances depending on the plant and time of assembly. The frontal and rear side armour sections featured a distinctive mid-side join, which was also riveted or welded according to the plant and time period concerned.

The turret was octagonal in shape, with varying forms and 15mm base armour thickness, later up-armoured at the production stage to 25mm by adding 10mm sheet armour to the base armour. Turrets produced at Sverdlovsk had a specific turret shape with an additional turret fillet behind the gun-mantlet and a different turret profile. There are also variations in the design of gun mantlets and other armoured components. The hulls and turrets of most T-60s were "ekranirovanny" i.e "shielded" (the Russian literal translation) with additional armoured steel plate on the hull and turret.

The suspension was of the torsion bar type. The running gear consisted of four roadwheels and a rear idler that was either of the same type and diameter as the roadwheels or not depending on the plant and time period concerned. The roadwheels were of several types, the most common being stamped and welded disc or cast types with rubber rims, though all

cast wheels with internal amortization were also fitted on some tanks. The T-60 was fitted with 260mm wide cast tracks, with 87 track links per side when new.

With several assembly plants involved in T-60 production, several armour plants producing hull and turret sets for the assembly plants, and tanks being assembled with whatever components were available at the time of assembly of any given T-60 tank, the detail appearance of the T-60 varied considerably according to the assembly plant, the availability of components and the time of production. Many tanks had up-armoured hulls, or turrets, or both. Roadwheels and idler wheels were solid disc or cast spoked, the latter with or sometimes without rubber rims. The drive sprockets were with or without removable sprocket rings. The exhaust systems were either the design rear exhaust tube with silencer mounted on the hull rear, or might be a simplified (and significantly noisier) fantail type. Although superficially identical, due to the number of plants involved in assembly and the number of components that fell in and out of availability due to the war situation, the T-60 as a tank type has an infinite variety of detail differences between individual tanks.

GENERAL LAYOUT

This T-60 tank located at the Muzei Tekhniki (the Vadim Zadorozhny Museum) located at Ilyinskoye, near Krasnogorsk in the western suburbs of Moscow, was produced at the relocated Plant N°37 in Sverdlovsk. It was rebuilt from three separate T-60 tank wrecks recovered in the Leningrad region. The turret number, and slogans "Za Stalina" (for Stalin) and "Za Leningrad" (for Leningrad) were still visible on the original turrets when recovered. The tank was the first T-60 restoration carried out in the Russian Federation, and as seen here, the tank is in running condition. (Andrey Aksenov)

HULL

The T-60 air intake and exhaust arrangement. Note the simplified "fantail" exhaust without silencer on this particular tank.

The two types of standard exhaust are shown here, the full system with silencer (left) and the simplified, and significantly louder fantail type (right) The radiator shields were used in cold weather for maintaining engine temperature. The circular hatches cover the fuel filler caps.

The T-60 track guards were relatively highly engineered considering the era in which they were produced.

The T-60 was used to tow light artillery such as 45mm and 57mm anti-tank guns. Tow hooks were either cast or machined on different tanks.

The simplified "fantail" exhaust as fitted to many T-60 tanks.

The rounded track guards were well engineered items requiring multiple stages in their finishing.

HULL

The T-60 had several types of driver-mechanic's hatch design depending on the plant and assembly time period. The headlight and signal horn were standard automotive fittings.

The driver-mechanic's hatch and locking lever.

The driver-mechanic's "rubka" and vision device.

The plant and time of production led to significant variances in components used, as seen here with the driver-mechanic's hatch. The driver-mechanic's visor had a bulletproof glass vision block.

The side armour had a distinct join between the front and rear plates, originally riveted and later welded. Note the difference in track pitch.

The T-60 was fitted out with various hand tools, including the axe seen here mounted on the right track guard.

The automotive type hydraulic jacking tool and spare track links mounted on the glacis.

TURRET & ARMAMENT

The octagonal T-60 turret was a distinctive feature of the T-60.

The 20mm TNSh gun barrel on this tank is not original.

The T-60 turret was diminutive, offering little room for the commander/gunner to operate. The original hatch type (right) was later replaced by the simplified version (left)

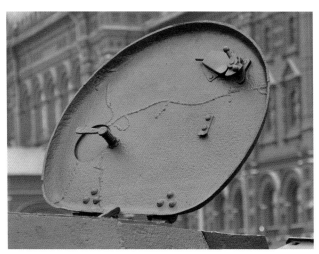

The turret features such as hatches, mantlets and ventilator domes varied between individual T-60 tanks. T-60 tanks originally had no ventilation, and only a small port for signal flare or flag use.

The T-60 turret finish and gun mantlet arrangements also varied from tank to tank. The up-armoured turrets are evident when looking at the respective surface or "countersunk" position of the pistol ports.

The 20mm TNSh was an effective weapon at close range.

The TNSh gun mantlet was welded together from individual armour plates.

The gun mantlet design also varied considerably between tanks and a different periods in construction. This gun mantlet is one of the most standard in appearance.

TURRET & ARMAMENT

The T-60 turret was a cramped working space for the commander who also worked as gunner and loader.

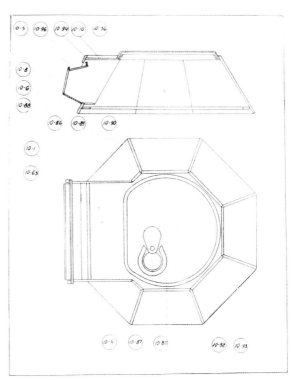

This original construction drawing clearly shows the distinctly hexagonal shape of the T-60 turret.

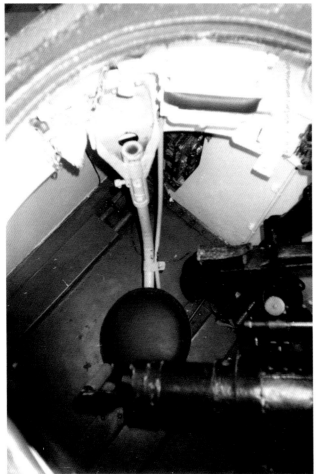

The T-60 was a tight fit internally, even more so with a full ammunition complement.

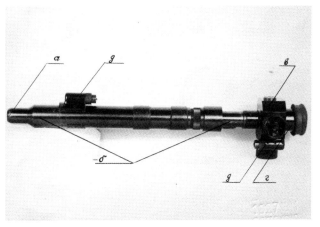

The TMPF-1 periscope gun sight as used on the T-60.

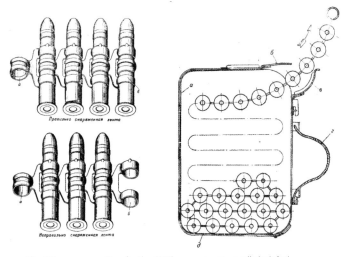

The 20mm ammunition for the TNSh cannon was usually belt fed in practice.

Clamping the armour plates of a T-60 turret before welding.

The TNSh was provided with purpose designed armour piercing rounds

The view from the commander/gunner's TMPF-1 sight reticule.

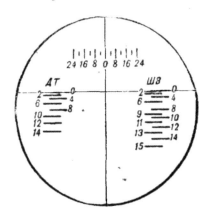

ENGINE & MECHANICS

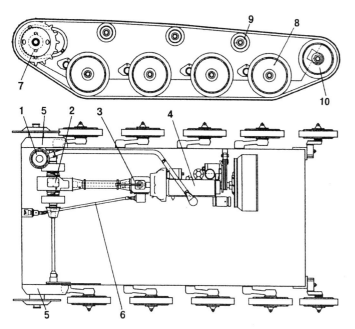

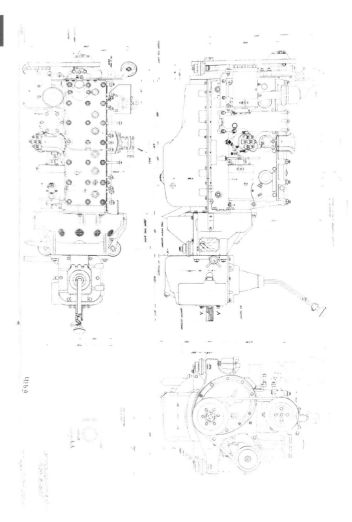

The T-60 was powered by a GAZ-202 automotive engine mounted together with the gearbox on the right side of the tank., with the drive sprockets being located at the front of the tank.

1. Air Filter 2. Main Drive 3. Gearbox 4. Engine 5. Side Friction Clutches 6. Starting Crank 7. Drive Sprocket 8. Road Wheels 9. Return Rollers 10. Rear Idler.

Plant drawing of the GAZ-202 engine.

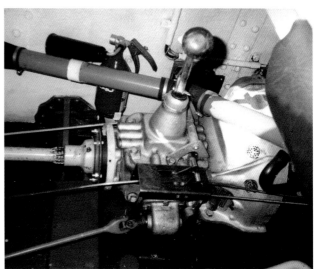

The automotive origin driver-mechanic's gear selector on the T-60.

The majority of T-60 tanks were fitted with either stamped disc or cast spoked roadwheels, both fitted with rubber rims; however all-steel roadwheels were also used on some tanks. The drive sprocket originally featured a replaceable drive gear ring, later deleted, while the idler, which was originally a specific design was later replaced by a standard roadwheel.

Rubber lined stop blocks were located on the first and last wheel stations.

The red painted bolts indicated lubrication points.

This tank has a cast final drive housing.

Early type stamped wheels can be seen on this T-60 located at the Parola Tank Museum, Finland.

Chapter 8

T-60 Preserved Tanks

In 1943, the Red Army liberated the village of Gluboky in the Rostov on Don Oblast (region), with T-60 tanks participating in the operation. One T-60 tank, which was presumably destroyed in combat during the engagement, remained in the village where in 1949 it was installed on a low plinth as a war memorial. This was the first, and as far as is known, the only complete T-60 to have been used for such a purpose. It is also one of the earliest Soviet plinth mounted tank memorials, which became common in the aftermath of the war. The tank was originally installed without tracks, but was later fitted with tracks from a DT-75 tracked agricultural tractor. The existen-

ce of this memorial became known outside Russia only in the 1990s after the break-up of the Soviet Union.

In the late 1940s and early 1950s a T-60 was exhibited at the Museum of the Defence of Leningrad. The tank, which was put on display in March 1947, was involved in operations starting in January 1943 to break the Siege of Leningrad, the tank being commanded by Lt. D.I. Osatyuk (see chapter 5). The museum was disbanded in the 1950s and the subsequent fate of the T-60 is unknown.

For many years the only known T-60 outside the Soviet Union was that located at the Parola Tank Museum in Finland,

A restored T-60 crosses Red Square on 7th November 2012, during a re-enactment of the historic 7th November 1941 parade, during which T-60s of the 33rd Tank Brigade joined T-34 medium and KV heavy tanks on Red Square, before moving directly to the front line only a few kilometres away. The tank commander is Vadim Zadorozhny who restored this and many other Russian tanks in recent years. He is wearing a pre-war tank officer's uniform. (Andrey Aksenov)

one of several captured by the Finns during the Russo-Finnish "Continuation War" of 1944 during which an eclectic mix of armour was used by the Red Army. The Parola T-60, which is fitted with a reproduction gun and mantlet, deteriorated badly over several decades of being displayed in the open but has recently been partially restored.

At the end of the 1980s the existence of the formerly secret tank museum at Kubinka west of Moscow became known outside the Soviet Union. The Kubinka museum, formerly part of the NIII-38 Institute and test polygon located at Kubinka

has a T-60, now in running order, which is believed to be an original prototype used for evaluation trials. The tank was recently moved to a new location at the new "Patriot Park" exhibition complex close to the original Kubinka site.

At the very beginning of the 21st Century a T-60 was restored to running condition by the Muzei Tekhniki (Vadim Zadorozhny Museum) located at Arkhangelskoe, near Krasnogorsk in the western suburbs of Moscow. This tank was often seen at exhibitions and shows and is now located within the main museum building. Subsequently, the same museum built

A T-60 parked on Red Square during an early morning rehearsal for the 7th November 2013 historic re-enactment of the 7th November 1941 parade. (Andrey Aksenov)

several (at least six) T-60 tanks, each of which used a few original recovered parts, but involving an industrial scale rebuilding effort including the manufacture from scratch of almost all the parts required for the T-60, from armour plate sections to the casting of new tracks using recovered original track links as the prototype for the sand cast moulds. All of these T-60 tanks are in running condition, powered by relatively modern automobile engines, and have since 2011 taken part in the annual 7th November military parade on Red Square which today commemorates the 7th November 1941 parade from which the participants went directly to the front line only a few kilometres away, rather than the Great October Revolution as before. These tanks also occasionally appear at exhibitions around Moscow.

At the turn of the 21st Century, a T-60 was located on the riverbed of the river Dobraya near Volgograd. The tank, of the type produced at Plant №264 in Krasnoarmeisk, was recovered and subsequently restored at the Volgograd Shipbuilding Plant, which, as the former Plant №264, is where the tank had been originally assembled some seven decades earlier. The tank is now on display at the Battle of Stalingrad museum complex in central Volgograd.

Also at the turn of the 21st Century, the Museum of Military Glory at Verkhnaya Pyshma, near Ekaterinburg, transformed from a small outdoor collection of tanks and military vehicles into an industrial scale museum complex. The museum has rebuilt from original drawings many tanks that were previously extinct, including such rarities as the T-34-57 and early KV-2, with the use of heavy gauge steel in their authentic reconstruction, something that only a "museum" with a former tank production facility virtually on-site, and with historically inclined management and accountants could even contemplate. The museum has two T-60 replica tanks on display, one a standard line tank, and the other a recreation of the M-8 (BM-8-24) multiple rocket launcher. The Museum of Russian Military History at Padikovo near Moscow also has a T-60 replica in running condition.

In the 1960s, the Vyksunsky plant, which had built hull and turret sets for the T-60 during the war reconstructed a T-60 which was displayed in their plant museum.

Another T-60 parked on Red Square during historic parade rehearsals, November 2013. The hulls and turrets of these restored tanks are original, but the engines, transmissions, wheels and tracks are all newly produced or re-manufactured. (Andrey Aksenov)

In addition there are several museum collections in Russian which have partly restored T-60 projects underway, and many hulls, turrets and parts have been recovered from battlefields in recent years, such that the T-60 has gone from being relatively obscure in terms of tanks available for inspection to now being a common sight in Russian museums and even at shows and exhibitions. The standard proviso that all museum restorations need to be treated with caution, (as the tanks are rebuilt from a mix of what has been recovered together with newly built parts, and are often a hybrid mix of components) applies to these restored tanks. The extensive material made recently available from Russian archives now however goes a long way to ensuring that the original appearance and fit-out of these once obscure tanks seen only in a wrecked state on the battlefield is now clearly understood, together with where they were made and under what conditions.

T-60 tanks parked behind T-37 amphibious tanks awaiting a 7th November 1941 historic parade rehearsal in Moscow, 2011.

T-60 tanks traverse Red Square, 7th November 2012. The post-war GAZ-51 engine was derived from the war-time GAZ-202. (Andrey Aksenov)

T-60 tanks entering Red Square during the 7th November 2012 historical re-enactment parade. (Andrey Aksenov)

PRESERVED T-60 TANKS

COUNTRY & CITY	LOCATION	DESCRIPTION
Australia, Cairns, Queensland	Australian Army & Artillery Museum	A T-60 restored in the Russian Federation and exported to Australia. The museum also has a T-70.
Finland, Parola	Parola Tank Museum	T-60 captured during the 1944 "Continuation War". Now partly restored, missing the original gun and gun mantlet
Russian Federation		
Arkhangelskoe, Krasnogorsk, Moscow Oblast	Muzei Tekhniki (Vadim Zadorozhny Museum)	T-60 restored to running order within the museum building, 6 other restored T-60s located outside, plus turrets and parts
Gluboky, Rostov Oblast		T-60 plinth mounted as a war memorial
Kubinka, Moscow Oblast	Patriot Park	T-60 formerly located at the NIII-38 Institute Kubinka Tank Museum
Moscow	Victory Park - Paklonnaya Gora	T-60 rebuit from a recovered wreck. Poor restoration with many incorrect features
Padikovo, Moscow Oblast	Museum of Russian Military History	T-60 replica restored to running condition
Tsemena, Novgorod Oblast		T-60 turret mounted on a brick plinth as a war memorial
Verkhnaya Pyshma, Sverdlovsk Oblast	Museum of Military Glory	T-60 replica rebuilt by the museum attached to what the UVZ plant, better known as Uralmash
Verkhnaya Pyshma, Sverdlovsk Oblast	Museum of Military Glory	T-60 BM-8 MRS rebuilt by the museum attached to what the UVZ plant
Volgograd	Volgograd Military Memorial Museum	T-60 on display outside the museum. Located in a local tributary of the Volga and restored by the plant (wartime No. 264) where it was built
Vsevolozhsk, Leningrad Oblast	National Automobile Museum	T-60 wreck, consisting of a hull and turret. Awaiting restoration

There are also some T-60 tanks in private collections, such as the T-60 in the collection of Igor Shishkin.
For the most definitive listing of preserved tanks worldwide, the authors recommend the following excellent website: theshadock.free.fr

MUZEI TEKHNIKI

The T-60 Plant N°37 (Sverdlovsk) restored by the Muzei Tekhniki (the Vadim Zadorozhny Museum) near Krasnogorsk during its first trial run after restoration to running condition.

KUBINKA

The T-60 located at Kubinka has also now been retored to running condition. It is believed to be one of the original T-60 prototypes evaluated for service with the Red Army, and served in the defence of the immediate region of Kubinka during the Battle of Moscow in the late autumn of 1941.

VERKHNAYA PYSHMA

The T-60 located at the Museum of Military Glory at Verknie Pyshma has now been relocated within the main museum buildings.

POKLONNAYA GORA MOSCOW

The T-60 recently added to the Great Patriotic War Museum collection at Poklonnaya Gora in Moscow is far from an ideal restoration, but indicative of the T-60 type in general.

PAROLA

Until relatively recently, the T-60 tank located at the Parola Tank Museum in Finland was the best known T-60 in existance, and the only one which until the fall of the Soviet Union was readily accessible. The tank has a false gun mantlet and armament. The tank has sufferd the ravages of being displayed in the open for decades.

MUSEUM OF RUSSIAN MILITARY HISTORY, PADIKOVO

This T-60 replica, based on many original components, is located at the Museum of Russian Military History, Padikovo, near Krasnogorsk in the western suburbs of Moscow.

On the Move...

The first T-60 restored by the Muzei Tekhniki (the Vadim Zadorozhny Museum) during a public display, showing its mobility. (All photos Andrey Aksenov)

T-60 tanks on parade in Moscow during 7th November 1941 Red Square commemorative displays.

Andrey Aksenov

Andrey Aksenov

T-60 N°216 UP-ARMOURED PLANT N°38 PRODUCTION

T-60 with additional armour, built by Plant N°38 in the Spring of 1942. Unknown Red Army unit. The tank is fitted with an asbestos protected exhaust pipe and automotive type silencer, but still has the cast road wheels used on earlier series procuction tanks.

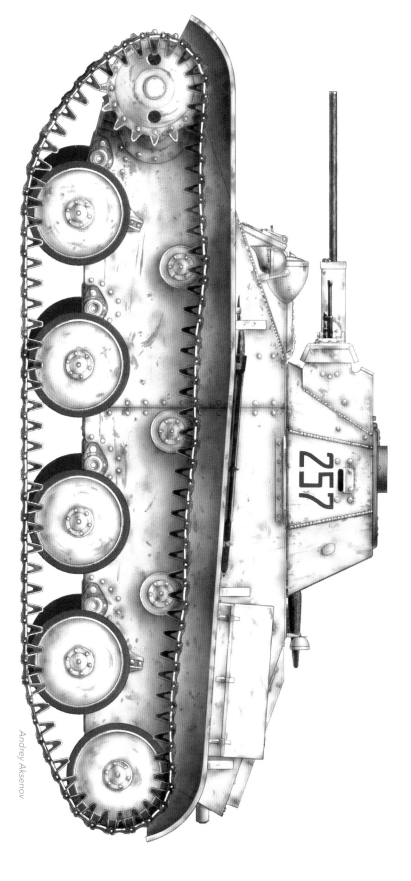

T-60 Nº257 PLANT Nº37 PRODUCTION

T-60 built by plant Nº37. The tank is painted in overall winter whitewash camouflage, 61st Tank Brigade, Leningrad Front, January 1943.

Andrey Aksenov

Andrey Aksenov

T-60 N°10-61 GAZ PRODUCTION

T-60 built by the GAZ plant in March–April 1942, unknown unit, battle for Kharkov, May 1942

T-60 GAZ PRODUCTION

T-60 from the initial series production batch built by GAZ, fitted with the conical turret from the T-30, 33rd Tank Brigade, Red Square, Moscow, 7th November 1941 Parade.

Andrey Aksenov

Andrey Aksenov

T-60 N°14-128 PLANT N°264 PRODUCTION

T-60 built by plant N°264, unknown unit, captured by Italian troops in the Summer of 1942.

T-60 Nº3672 PLANT Nº264 PRODUCTION

T-60 built by Plant Nº264, Stalingrad 1942, unknown unit, destroyed in combat against the German 100th Jaeger Division, Stalingrad area, late summer 1942.

Andrey Aksenov

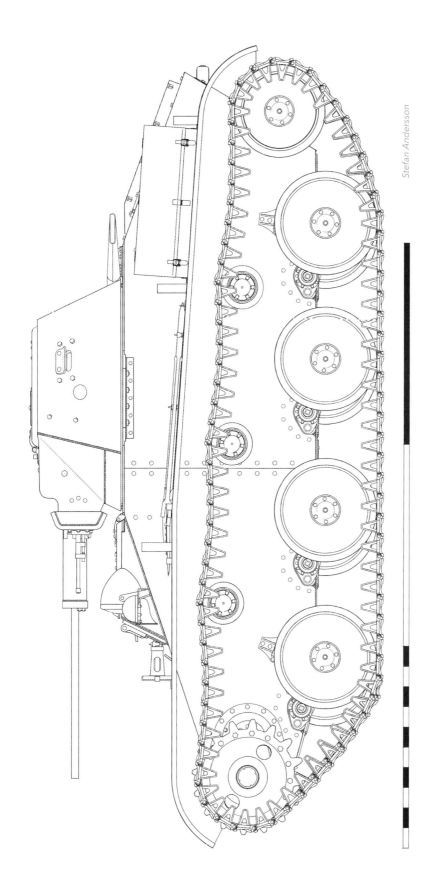

Stefan Andersson

T-60, GAZ INITIAL PRODUCTION

T-60 of GAZ initial production batch, fitted with the conical T-30 turret, autumn 1941.

T-60, GAZ PRODUCTION

A typical T-60 produced at GAZ, November - December 1941.

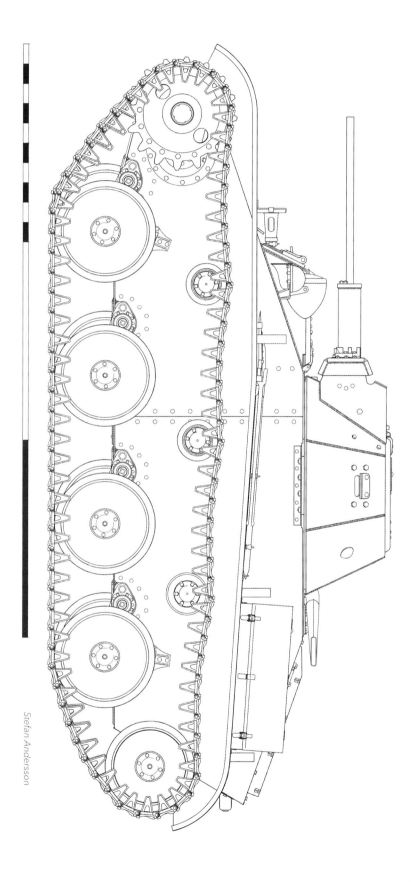

Stefan Andersson

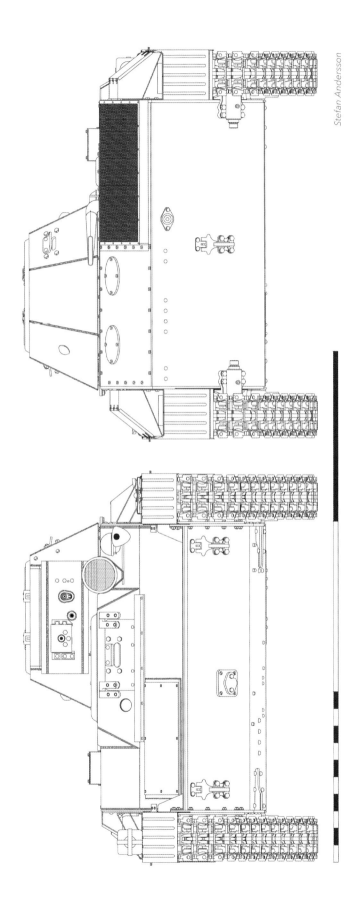

Stefan Andersson

T-60, GAZ PRODUCTION

Front, rear and plan elevations of a typical T-60 produced at GAZ, November - December 1941.

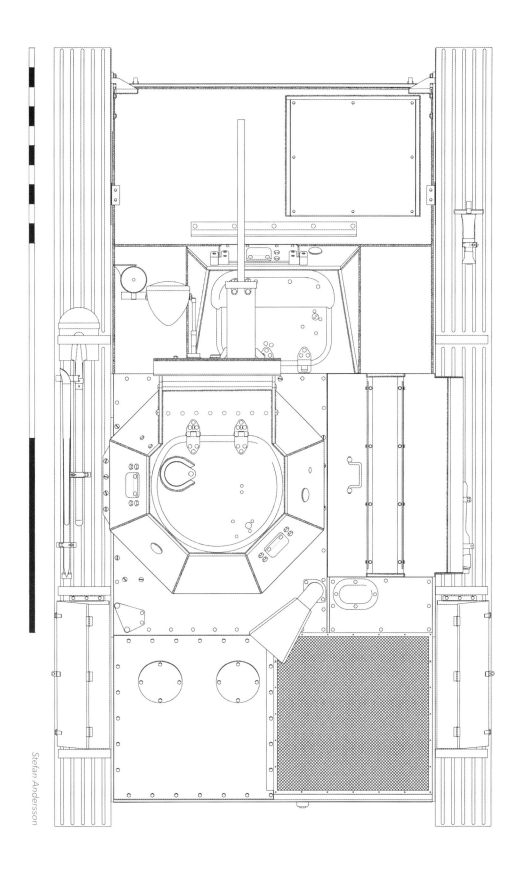

Stefan Andersson

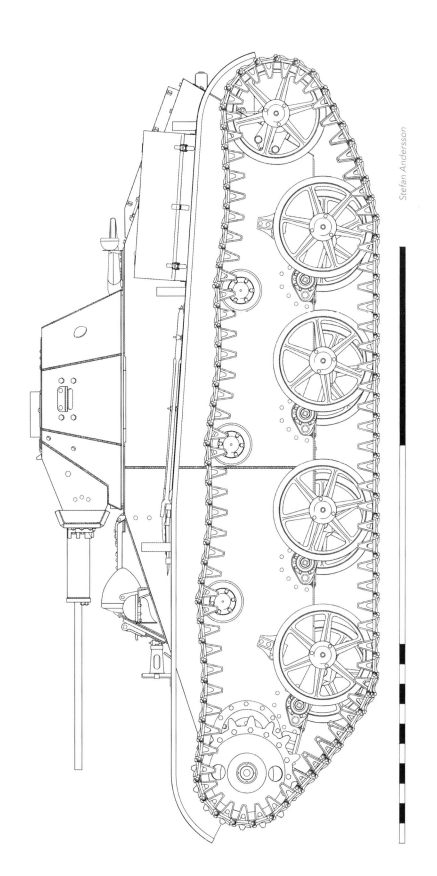

Stefan Andersson

T-60, PLANT N°37 (SVERDLOVSK)

T-60 produced at the relocated Plant N°37 (Sverdlovsk) in the summer of 1942.

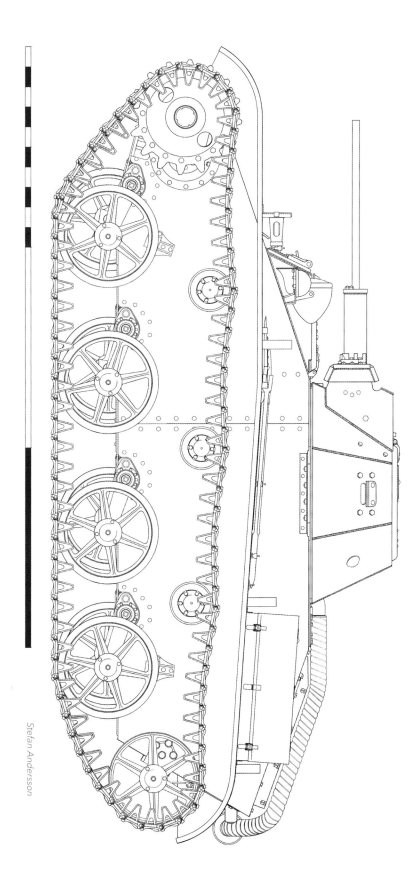

T-60, PLANT Nº38 (KIROV)

T-60 produced at Plant Nº38 (Kirov) in the spring-summer of 1942.

Stefan Andersson

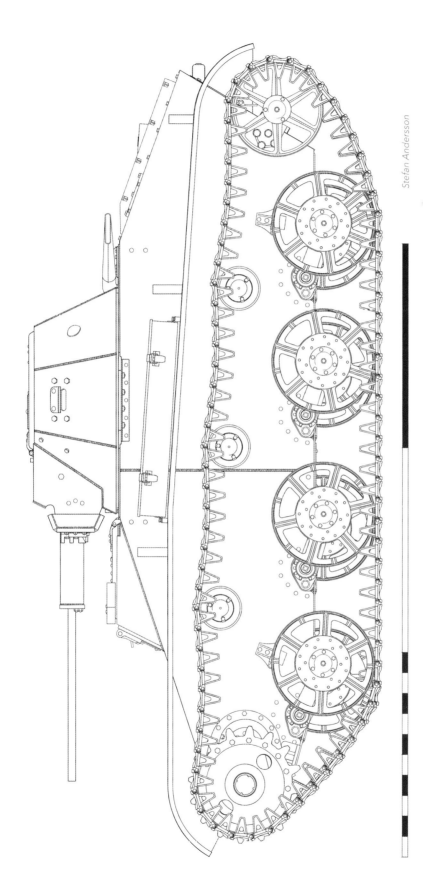

Stefan Andersson

T-60, PLANT N°264

T-60 produced at Plant N°264 in the summer of 1942.

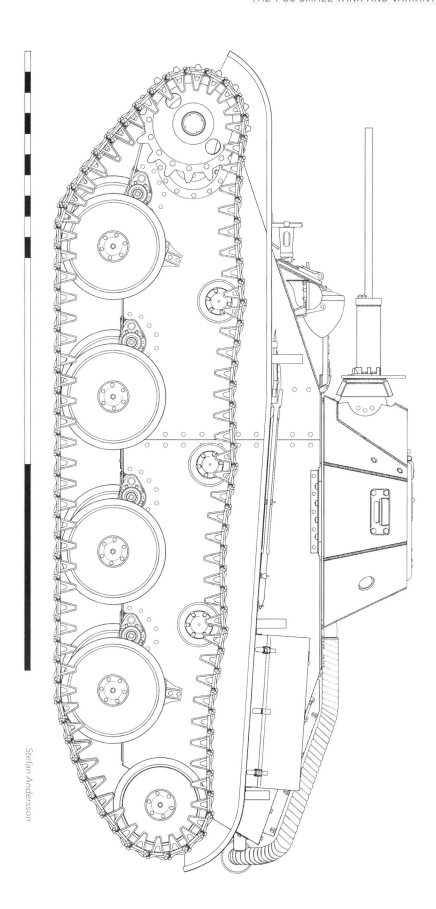

T-60, GAZ PRODUCTION

T-60 with screened "ekranami" armour, GAZ production, spring 1942.

Stefan Andersson

Appendix and Data Tables

Appendix 1

Technical Summary Technical characteristics of the armoured hull of the T-60 light tank under fire from domestic anti-tank weapons (unplanned work).

E.E. Levin - Chief Engineer TsNII-48, G.I. Kapirin - Chief of Production Sector.

The above-cited report, by E.E. Levin, senior engineer at TsNII-48, and G.I. Kapirin reviewed the results of testing the armour of the T-60 with fire from typical anti-tank projectiles, as was standard practice with all Soviet tank designs.

The hull for these tests was provided by the "Red October" plant, welded and then subjected to heat treatment in a low temperature oven to obtain the required armour hardness.

Polygon testing was conducted with domestic small calibre armour-piercing rounds - the 7.62mm B-30, 12.7mm DK, 14.5mm B-32 (from the PTRD anti-tank rifle), and anti-tank rounds from 37mm and 45mm anti-tank guns.

The 7.62mm B-30 rounds were fired against the 15mm side armour, 10mm rear armour, and the 6mm lower frontal armour. Firing trials showed the T-60 to be invulnerable to the 7.62mm B-30 round at all ranges and angles of fire. The results of fire from the 12.7mm DK and 14.5 mm B-32 armour-piercing rounds were shown in diagram format, showing the ranges from which the T-60 was invulnerable which was basically all but very close range.

The 35mm glacis armour was tested against fire from a Soviet 45mm anti-tank gun, which showed that the strength of components and welded joints, and the overall hull survivability from fire by 37 and 45 mm anti-tank rounds was considered acceptable. Some components proved unsatisfactory, including the "rubka" armour protection for the driver-mechanic, while the mountings for various components (tow hooks, hatches, access hatches, etc.), were destroyed by shell fire, these components being modified in T-60 and subsequent T-70 series production.

The conclusions were that the T-60 was invulnerable to fire from 7.62-7.92 mm calibre ammunition from any distance, and against 12.7-13mm rounds at any distance against the frontal armour within an angle of 120° from vertical and against large-calibre machine guns of 14.5-15mm calibre head-on at any distance within an angle of 80° from vertical. The calibres quotes included for Soviet and German weapons. As regards 37mm anti-tank fire, the frontal armour provided protection at ranges above 650m and at an angle of 80° from vertical. As expected, protection from 45mm anti-tank fire against the frontal armour, the T-60 was invulnerable only at distances of more than 700-1000m with an angle of 40-50° from the vertical, in other words the tank was vulnerable at all typical engagement ranges.

The side armour of the T-60 (and the T-70, tested simultaneously) was noted as being particularly weak, providing protection against 7.62mm-7.92mm armour-piercing rounds only.

The report conclude that:

"The results of the strength of individual components and sub-assemblies have been incorporated in the mass production of T-60 light tanks at the "Red October", №264 and №180 plants".

Appendix 2

T-60 production simplifications introduced by GAZ, 11th November 1941:

- Use of radiators with internal pipework varying from 7mm to 11 mm in diameter.
- Replacement of copper fuel and oil lines with brass or steel.
- Replacement of cast/machined radiator and fuel tank parts with stamped units built at GAZ.
- Replace the cast aluminum fan with duraluminium blades with stamped steel alternatives.
- Replace the MK-3-6MG carburetor with other carburetors (K-23, M-1, etc) as available.
- Replace lead-lined galvanized steel fuels tank with unprotected sheet steel.
- Cancel the ammeter and voltmeter and replace the first warning light.
- Cancel shielding of electrical equipment and wiring on line tanks (i.e. those without radio).
- Replace headlights and tail lights with standard vehicle types.
- Simplify the separate fuses in the circuits and cheapen their construction.
- Replace ebony battery cases with plastic if required.
- Cancel the signal horn if required.
- Change the generator and relay types according to available supply.
- Review and reduce the driver-mechanic's tool set.
- Cancel the clock if needs dictate.
- Reduce the number of lamps within the tank (including the sight)
- Cancel in case of emergency disconnect switch.
- Simplify the exhaust system.
- Cancel installation of the oil cooler in winter.
- Cancel ventilation of the engine crankcase in winter (connected to the fuel supply system).
- Cancel the turret hatch sealing rubber if required.
- Cancel the rubber engine mounts and rigidly mount the engine.
- Allow the delivery of tanks with a mechanical sight (in the absence of optics)
- Cancel the holes on the underside of the suspension bracket and two holes on the side (reducing the number of riveting operations required by 56 rivets on each tank).
- Cancel the rubber rim on the rear idler, using instead cast rollers or disc rollers, or rimless rollers with a smooth (machined smooth) rim surface.
- Make the drive sprocket of cast design, without a stamped drive ring and 16 locating bolts.
- Review and minimize the ZIP (spare parts) kits.

T-60 Data Table

TANK	T-60	T-60 (Up-armoured)	T-45	T-60-Z	SZU
Lenght (mm)	4100	4100	4100	4100	4100
Width (mm)	2290	2290	2290	2290	2290
Height (mm)	1750	1750	1750	1750	1750
Track (mm)	1660	1660	1660	1660	1660
Clearance (mm)	300	300	300	300	300
Track width (mm)	260	260	260	260	260
Combat weight (kg)	5800	6200	6800	6500	6420
Crew	2	2	2	2	2
HULL ARMOUR					
Upper glacis (mm/°)	15/65	25/65	25/65	15/65	15/65
Driver's "rubka" (mm/°)	20/70	35/70	35/70	20+15/70	20+15/70
Lower glacis (mm/°)	10/15	35/15	10/15	10/15	10/15
Upper rear (mm/°)	13/76	15/76	15/76	15/76	15/76
Lower rear (mm/°)	13/30	25/30	15/30	13+10/30	13+10/30
Roof (mm/°)	13/0	15/0	15/0	13/0	13/0
Floor (mm/°)	6-10/0	6-10/0	6-10/0	6-10/0	6-10/0
TURRET ARMOUR					
Front (mm/°)	20/90	25-35/90	35/90	25/90	35/90
Side (mm/°)	15/25	25/25	35/25	25/25	35/25
Rear (mm/°)	25/25	25/25	35/25	25/25	35/27
Roof (mm/°)	10/0	10/0	10/0	–	10/0 (foldable)
Armament	1 x 20mm TNSh 1 x 7,62mm DT	1 x 20mm TNSh 1 x 7,62mm DT	1 x 45mm M-38 20K 1 x 7,62mm DT	2 x 12,7mm DShK	2 x 12,7mm DShKT
Ammunition	780 x 20mm 945 x 7,62mm	780 x 20mm 945 x 7,62mm	66 x 45mm 945 x 7,62mm	360 x 12,7mm	480 x 12,7mm
Elevation (°)	+25/-7	+25/-7	+20/-6	+65/-7	+70/-4,3
Traverse (°)	360	360	360	360	360
Sights	TMFP	TMFP	TOP	TMFP K-8T	TMFP K8T
Communications	Signal, Flag	Signal, Flag	Signal, Flag	Signal, Flag	12-R radio
Configuration	6 in line	6 in line	6 in line	6 in line	6 in line
Dispacement (cm³)	3480	3480	5555	5555	3480
Engine	GAZ-202, petrol	GAZ-202, petrol	ZiS-16, petrol	ZiS-16, petrol	GAZ-202, petrol
Power output (hp)	70	70	85	85	70
Gearbox	4sp	4sp	4sp	4sp	4sp
Max. Speed (road/terrain)	45/25 km/h	45/25 km/h	41/33 km/h	41/33 km/h	45/25 km/h
Range (road/terrain)	300/285 km	300/280 km	300/280 km	300/280 km	300/280 km
Trench (mm)	900	900	900	900	900
Maximum slope (°)	29	29	36	36	29

T-60 Production

	37	KhTZ	GAZ	264	37	38
PLANT LOCATION	Moscow	Kharkov	Gorky	Krasnoarmeisk	Sverdlovsk	Kirov
1941						
August	1					
September	1+	7	3	1		
October	244?	Captured	215	?		
November	Evacuated		471	?		
December	Evacuated		634 / 625	52	11 / 22	
Total for 1941	245*		1323 / 1314	?	?	
1942						
January			?	102	0	1
February			?	?	67**	80
March			320****	249 for Q1 1942	165	160
April			138	?	190^^^	?
May			?	?	280	?
June			830 to 6.42	830 total in 42 to 6/42	321	22+10 (M8)
July				51	10	25
August					0	
September					0	
October					50-55	
November						
December					25	
Total for 1942			2913	1174	1033 / 1144	524+10 (M8)
1943						
January					11	
February					44	
Total for 1943					55	
Total build (all plants) 5662 (5839)						
Total delivered to Red Army 5796						

*Plant №37 (Moscow) built T-30 and T-60 tanks to 26.10.41 prior to evacuation to Sverdlovsk. Recent material suggests the October production is disputed

**Plant №37 (Sverdlovsk) built 147 T-30 & T-60 tanks in February 1942, of which 67 were T-60

*** Plant №37 (Sverdlovsk) built 190 T-60s in April 1942, but 86 were without tracks

**** GAZ built 1639 T-60s in the first three months of 1942

T-60 based Armoured Trailers & Sleds

DESIGNATION	TD-200	TD-2	BP-60
Weight (empty, kg)	8000	4625 (3975)	3000
Weight (combat, kg)	10000	5750 (5100)	4000
Lenght (mm)	4510	3305	3900
Width (mm)	2576	2578	1770
Height (mm)	1485	1400	1220
Ground clearance (mm)	350	400	170
Desant crew	20	15	10
ARMOUR (mm/°)			
Upper glacis	30/31	30/30 (20/30)	25/65
Lower glacis	30/33	30/30,5 (20/30,5)	10/15
Side	40/90	40/90	15/90
Rear	30/31	30/30 (20/30)	15/30
Roof	20/0	20/0	15/0
Floor	15/0	15/0	6-10/0

T-60 Assembly and Component Production Plants, by Plant Number

Plant №2 (Kovrov) - The "Kirkizh" Plant - 20mm TNSh automatic cannon

Plant №34 (Moscow) - radiators and other components

Plant №37 (Moscow, then relocated to Sverdlovsk) - T-60 assembly

Plant №38 (Kirov) - T-60 assembly

Plant №69 (Krasnogorsk) - The "Lenin" plant -TMFP gun sights and optics

Plant №76 (Stalingrad) - The Stalingrad Tractor Plant (STZ)

Plant №92 (Gorky) - the "Novoe Sormovo" (artillery) plant

Plant №112 (Gorky) - the "Krasnoye Sormovo" Plant - Armour plate production

Plant №113 (Gorky) - the Milling Machine Plant, Gorky (BM-8-24 on T-60 chassis)

Plant №176 (Murom) - the Dzerzhinsky Steam Locomotive Plant - Hull and Turret sets

Plant №177 (Vyksa) - Vyksunsky DRO Plant - Hull and Turret Sets

Plant №178 (Kulebaki, nr. Saratov) - the Kulebakski "S.M. Kirov" Plant - Hull and Turret sets

Plant №180 (Saratov) - the Saratov Rail Wagon Repair Plant - Hull & Turret sets

Plant №200 (Chelyabinsk) – TD-200 "Bronesani" armoured trailer sleds

Plant №264 (Krasnoarmeisk) - T-60 hull and Turret sets and tank assembly

Plant №469 (Gorky) - the "Gromov" Plant

Plant №507 (Lopasnaya) - DShK heavy machine guns

Plant №535 (Tula) - The Tula Armaments Plant - 20mm ShVAK/TNSh automatic cannon

Plant №592 (Mytischi) - Mytischi Machine Building Plant (MMZ) - T-60 components

Plant №733 (Moscow) - the "Kompressor" Plant - M8 (BM-8-24) MRS on T-60 chassis

T-60 Assembly and Component Production Plants, by Plant Name

GAZ "Molotov" Plant (Gorky) - T-60 assembly, engines, components for other plants

Izhorsky plant (Kolpino) - T-60 hull and turret sets

Kovrovsky Zavod №2 (Kovrov) - 20mm ShVAK/TNSh automatic cannon

KhEMZ (ХЭМЗ) - Kharkov Electromechanical Plant - T-60 components

KhTZ (ХТЗ) - Kharkov Tractor Plant - T-60 assembly

KhGTZ (ХТТЗ) - Kharkov "Kirov" Turbo-Generator Plant - T-60 components

Kolomensky "Kuibyshev" Machine Building Plant (KMZ Kolomna) - T-60 hull and turret sets

Kolomensky Paravozostroitelniy Zavod (KPZ Kolomna) - Kolomna Steam Locomotive Plant (KPZ)

Kompressor Plant (Moscow) (Plant №733) - mounted BM-8 MRS on T-30, T-60 tank and wheeled chassis

Krasny Kotelshchik Plant (Taganrog) - T-60 hull and turret sets

Krasniy Oktyabr Plant (Red October) Plant (Stalingrad) - T-60 hull & turret sets for Plant №264

Kuznetsky Metallurgichesky Zavod (Stalinsk - today Novokuznetsk) - Armour plate production

Murom Plant NKPS (Murom) - See Plant №176

Novo-Kramatorsky Plant NKTM (Novo-Kramatorsk) - T-60 hull & turret sets

October Revolution Plant NKTM (Voroshilovgrad) - T-60 hull & turret sets

Voroshilovgrad Plant (Vyksa) (Plant №177) - T-60 hull and turret sets

Vyksunsky Plant DRO - T-60 hull and turret sets

Yaroslavsky Shinny Zavod (Yaroslavl) - Rubber rims for roadwheels

Footnote: "Zavod" means plant or factory in Russian, the terms are interchangeable

Glossary

ABTU (АБТУ)	*Avtobronetankovoe Upravlenie (Auto-Tank Command)*
ANIOP	*Артиллерийский научно-исследовательский опытный полигон - Artillery Scientific Experimental Test Range*
ArtKom GAU KA (АртКом ГАУ КА)	*Artillery Committee Main Artillery Command of the Red Army*
BP	*Brone Pritsep (Bronepritsep) (armoured trailer)*
BTU (БТУ)	*Bronetankovoe Upravlenie - Tank Command*
DOT (ДОТ)	*Dolgovremennaya Ognevaya Tochka (hardened fire-point)(bunker)*
DP	*Desantny Pritsep - desant trailer*
GABTU KA (ГАБТУ КА)	*Glavnoye AvtoBronetankovoyea Upravlenye KA - Main Auto-Tank Command of the Red Army*
GAU	*Glavnoye Artilleriiskoye Upravleniye - State Artillery Directorate*
GAZ	*Gorky Avtomobilny Zavod - GAZ plant (named after Molotov)*
GKhP (ГХП)	*Gusenichniy Khimicheskii Pritsep - Tracked chemical trailer*
GKO	*Gosudarstnenny Komitet Oboroni - State Defence Committee of the USSR*
GVKhU (ГВХУ КА)	*Glavnoe Voenno-Khimicheskoe Upravlenie Krasnoi Armii - Main Military - Chemical Forces Directorate (of the Red Army)*
KA (КА)	*Krasnaya Armiya - Red Army (also known as RKKA)*
KB (КБ)	*Konstruktorskoye Bureau - Design Bureau*
KhEMZ	*Kharkov Electromekhanicheskiy Zavod - Kharkov Electromechanical plant*
KT (КТ)	*Krilya Tanka - Tank Wings or Flying Tank*
MRS	*Multiple Rocket System*
LII	*Letno-Issledovatelskiy Institut*
NATI	*Nationalniy Avtomobilniy Traktorniy Institut (National Auto-Tractor Institute)*
NKAP	*Narkomat Aviatsionnoi Promishlennosti.*
NKO	*Narodny Kommisariat Oboroni - State Defence Committee*
NKV	*People's Commissariat of Armaments*
NKSM	*Ministry of Medium Machine Building (Narkomsredmash) - responsible for tank production*
NKTM	*People's Commissariat of Heavy Engineering*
NKTP	*People's Commissariat of Tank Production*
OF	*Oskolochno-Fugasny - High-Explosive-Fragmentation)*
RGAEh (РГАЭ)	*Rossiskiy Gosudarstvenniyi Arkhiv Ekonomiki - Российский Государственной Архив - Russian State Economic Archives*
RGASPI (РГАСПИ)	*Rossiskiy Gosudarstvenniy Arkhiv Sotsialno-Politichesko Istorii - Russian State Archive of Social-Political History*
SAU (САУ)	*Samokhodnaya Art. Ustanovka - Self-Propelled Artillery Piece (SAU or SU)*
ShVAK (ШВАК)	*Shpitalny-Vladimirov Aviatsionnaya Krupnokalibernaya - Shpitalny-Vladimirov Heavy Calibre aviation (20mm cannon)*
SNK (СНК СССР)	*Sovet Narodnikh Kommissarov - Council of People's Commissars*
STZ (СТЗ)	*Stalingradskiy Traktorniy Zavod - Stalingrad Tractor Zavod*
SZU (СЗУ)	*Samokhodnaya Zenitnaya Ustanovka - Self-Propelled Anti-Aircraft System*
TD-200 (ТД-200)	*Transport Desantny Zavod 200 - Desant Tranporter Plant 200*
TsAGI	*Central Aerohydroynamics Institute*
TMFP (ТМФП)	*Teleskopicheskii Marona-Filkenshtein Pulemetny) - Telescopic Maron-Filkenshtein (machine gun) sight*
TNSh (ТНШ)	*Tankovaya Nudelmana-Shpitalnaya - Nudelman Shpitalny tank (20mm cannon) (TNSh, also known as TNSh-1, TNSh-20)*
TsAGI (ЦАГИ)	*Tsentralniy Aerogidrodinamicheskiy Institut - Central Aerodynamic Institute (TsAGI)*
TsaMO RF (ЦАМО РФ)	*Tsentralniy Arkhiv Ministerstva Oboroni Rossiskoi Federatsii - Central Archives of the Ministry of Defence of the Russian Federation*
TsVKP(b) (ЦК ВКП(б)	*Central Committee of the CPSU(b) - Communist Party (Bolshevik) of the USSR*
TTT	*Taktiko-Tekhnicheskiye Trebovaniya - Tactical Technical Tasks*
Voenizdat	*State Military Publisher NKO SSSR*
VVS KA	*Voenno-Vozdushniye Sili Krasnoi Armii - Red Army Air Force*
VYa-23 (ВЯ-23)	*VYa-23 23mm automatic cannon*
ZSU (ЗСУ)	*Zenitnaya Samokhodnaya Ustanovka - Self Propelled Ant-Aircraft Gun*

Notes
Desant - Literally "landing" troops, a description applied to tank borne infantry and to airborne forces

Ekranirovka (Экран, Экранировка) - A Russian term denoting the screening, or addition up-armouring of the base armour plate on a tank. Due to the complexities of Russian grammar, and the transliteration of the word depending on context, the word appears in many guises. The Russia letter "Э" also does not feature in the Roman alphabet, so can be transliterated as "Eh" or "E". For simplicity and ease of reading the term "ekranirovka" has been used throughout this book.

Korpus - Soviet production records refer to the building of "korpus" sets, which in Russian refers to a complete structure such as a building, or in the case of tanks, a complete hull and turret set, rather than just the hull.

Soviet Era Place Names
The city of Kharkiv in Ukraine is described in this book as Kharkov, by which Soviet Russian name it was known throughout the period of the Soviet Union. After the break up of the Soviet Union, several cities in Ukraine reverted to use of local Ukrainian language and spelling, such that Kharkov and Lvov reverted to Kharkiv and Lviv respectively. The spellings used in this book are consistent with the period in Soviet history being described.

Soviet Ministries
Soviet ministries were abbreviated to NK (Narodny Kommissariat - People's Commissariat) followed by the responsibility, e.g. NKV (Vooruzhenie - armaments), NKSM (Srednie Mashinostroeniye - medium machine building (actually tank production)) etc. The minister was known as the Narkom (Kommissar). Commissariat can be interpreted as Ministry, and Commissar as Minister

NKAP	*People's Commissariat of Aviation Production*
NKGK	*People's Commissariat of State Control*
NKO	*People's Commissariat of Defence*
NKS	*People's Commissariat of Machine Tool Building*
NKSM	*People's Commissariat of Medium (i.e. Tank) Machine Building*
NKSP	*People's Commissariat of Steel Production*
NKTM	*People's Commissariat of Heavy Engineering*
NKTP	*People's Commissariat of Heavy (i.e. Tank) Production in wartime*
NKTP	*People's Commissariat of Tank Production*
NKV	*People's Commissariat of Armaments*

Soviet Ministries - As written in the original Russian:

НКАП	Наркомат Авиационной промышленности - People's Commissariat of Aviation Industry	- NKAP
НКГК	Народный Комиссариат Государственного Контроля - People's Commissariat of State Control	- NKGK
НКС	Народный Комиссариат Станкостроению - People's Commissariat of Machine Tool Building	- NKS
НКСМ	Наркомат Среднего Машиностроения - People's Commissariat of Medium Machine Building	- NKSM
НКТП	Народный Комиссариат Танковой Промышленности - People's Commissariat of Tank Industry	- NKTP
НКВ	Народный Комиссариат Вооружения - People's Commissariat of Armaments	- NKV
НКТМ	Наркомат Тяжелого Машиностроения - People's Commissariat of Heavy Machine Building	- NKTM

Наркомат (Ministry) Народный (People's) are from the same word root, so are effectively interchangeable.

Photographic archives
Andrey Aksenov, Bair Irincheev, GAZ, James Kinnear, Maksim Kolomiets, RGAKF - Russian State Archive of Cinematic and Photographic Documentation, TsGAKFF - Central State Archive of Cinematic and Photographic Documentation, Yuri Pasholok, Igor Zheltov.

Note: the event dates where taken from the above archives are as noted on the official photograph index cards, which in most cases were compiled long after the date of the event and are not thereby always 100% accurate.

Bibliography

The bibliography for this book is relatively short in that no foreign references are used in this particular book due to the limited level of pre-existing research on the subject. The material used for this book comes almost exclusively from the archives of the Russian State organizations as noted at the beginning of the book.

Books

Baryatinsky, Mikhail, *Sovietskie Tanki v Boyu ot T-26 do IS-2. Eksmo, Moscow, 2007*
Baryatinsky, Mikhail, *Tanki Vtoroi Mirovoi, Eksmo, Moscow, 2009*
Drig, Evgenniy, *Mekhanizirovannie Korpus RKKA v Boyu, Transkniga, Moscow, 2005*
Kosirev,E.A, Orekhov, E.M, Fomin, N.N, *Tanki, Izdaletstvo DOSAAF, Moscow, 1973*
Pasholok, Yuri, *T-60 i Mashini Na Ego Baze, Tactical Press, Moscow, 2013*
Prochko. E.I. *Legkie Tanki T-40 i T-60, (Bronekollektsia №4) Modelist Konstruktor, Moscow, 1997*
Solyankin, A.G, Pavlov, M.V, Pavlov, I.V, Zheltov, I.G, *Otechestvennie Bronirovannie Mashini XX vek Tom 2 1941-45. Eksprint, Moscow. 2005*
Svirin, Mikhail, *Tanki Stalinsky Epokhi, Yauza, Eksmo, Moscow, 2001*

Journals & Magazines

MHobby
Soviet Military Review
Tekhnika i Vooruzhenie
Tekhnika Molodezhi

Author Biographies

James Kinnear was born in Great Britain on 11th August 1959, and has researched the topic of Soviet and Russian military hardware since his first visit to the enigmatic and mysterious Soviet Union as a young teenager in 1973. Having first visited the country when it was considered a threat, and all who travelled there as tourists were scrutinised as suspect communists back home in Blighty (rather than perhaps just having an appreciation for beautiful women), James subsequently lived and worked in the post-Soviet Russian Federation throughout the entire period of post-Soviet "stability" - the two decades between the Soviet Union being considered a military threat and the Russian Federation finding itself again categorized as such again in recent history.

James has written hundreds of articles on Soviet and Russian military technology. A Russian speaker, he has studied the subject from within the military intelligence community and as a civilian author. He is a formal contributor to IHS Jane's defence yearbooks and has published books on Soviet military technology with Barbarossa, Darlington, Osprey Vanguard and Tankograd. This is his first book for Canfora.

Yuri Pasholok was born on 2nd August 1979 in Moscow. He began to seriously study the history of armoured vehicles from 2002, when working as a historical consultant on various game projects relating to the Second World War. In 2005 Yuri also began work with a group of volunteers involved in the restoration of tanks at various museums, initially as a hobby and later on a professional basis.

From 2008 to 2013 Yuri worked within the Central Museum of the Great Patriotic War, during which time he also published his first book on armoured vehicles. Yuri's main focus is now the study of the development and history of Soviet armoured vehicles over the period 1920-1950. Yuri today continues to work as a consultant in computer game projects requiring professional historical research, on the basis that such games are today one of the best means to popularise the history of tank developement. This is his first book for Canfora.